D1133111

GENERAL'S LADY
The Life of Julia Grant

Other Books by Alice Fleming

DOCTORS IN PETTICOATS

GREAT WOMEN TEACHERS

WHEELS: FROM OX CARTS TO SPORTS CARS

GENERAL'S LADY
The Life of Julia Grant

by Alice Fleming

Illustrated by Richard Lebenson

J. B. LIPPINCOTT COMPANY
PHILADELPHIA / NEW YORK

PRINTED IN THE UNITED STATES OF AMERICA
LIBRARY OF CONGRESS CATALOG CARD NUMBER: 76-141457
FIRST EDITION

GENERAL'S LADY
The Life of Julia Grant

I

JULIA DENT perched on a stool by the kitchen table and watched Mary Robinson's strong black fingers briskly kneading a lump of dough and rolling it into what would soon be a flaky brown piecrust. The apples that would fill it had come from the Dents' own orchards. Mary and Julia had peeled them together, the slave woman deftly guiding the little girl's hands to be sure the sharp paring knife cut nothing more than the thin green apple skins.

It was not often that Julia could be coaxed into staying indoors and helping in the kitchen, but today she seemed to be enjoying herself. Her fingers were dusty with flour and there was a dab of cinnamon on her plump cheek. She watched carefully as Mary lifted a thin pancake of dough and pressed it gingerly into place in the pie pan.

"Now, the apples," Julia announced, passing Mary the brown earthenware bowl.

The woman took it and smiled at her small helper.

"It's nice to see you acting like a girl for a change," she said, "instead of skipping off to the woods to catch tadpoles with your brothers."

Julia laughed. Mary was always teasing her about being a tomboy. But with four older brothers, how could she be anything else?

John, the oldest of the boys, had taught Julia to pick up

bullfrogs; George had taught her how to bait a fishhook; Louis, who was closest to her own age, had taught her to climb trees; and Fred, her favorite, had taught her not to cry when she lost her footing and fell out of them.

There was only one thing that her brothers had not taught Julia Dent. It was the one thing she wanted to learn more than anything else—how to ride a horse. Julia's father kept a fine stable and all her brothers had learned to ride almost as soon as they had learned to walk.

The boys had gone off on horseback that very afternoon to watch the cavalry parade at Jefferson Barracks, five miles away. Julia, left alone, had retreated to the basement kitchen. But she hadn't fooled Mary Robinson with her sudden interest in making apple pies.

"Don't be impatient, Miss Julia," the slave said softly. "Colonel Dent's as anxious to get you up on horseback as you are to go. He's just waiting till you're a little bit bigger so you don't slip right out of the saddle."

Julia was ten but she was tiny for her age. Even Louis, the smallest of her four brothers, could easily boost her up on his shoulders and go jogging off to the woods where they usually played.

The Dents had a handsome brick town house in St. Louis but they preferred to spend most of their time at White Haven, their country estate about a dozen miles from the center of the city. White Haven was a low rambling farmhouse with wide stone chimneys. Two lines of locust trees flanked the long road that led from the stile where visitors hitched their horses to the broad veranda where the Dents liked to receive their guests.

Beyond the house with its slender pillars and long narrow windows, there was almost a thousand acres of land —carefully tended fields of alfalfa, wheat and corn, pasture lands for the cows and sheep, a barn and stables, and neat rows of trees in the apple orchards on the hillside. There were also several hundred acres of uncultivated wilderness, rolling meadowlands, thick woods, and shady groves where violets and wild strawberries nestled in the scraggly grass.

Julia Dent had been born at White Haven on January 26, 1826. Her black nurse, Annie, had told her about it so often that Julia knew the story by heart. There was a roaring fire in every fireplace against the bitter wintry weather but when Colonel Dent heard that his wife had just presented him with a baby daughter, he raced out as if it were mid-July to shout the good news to every slave on the farm. Annie's brother, Samuel, had been charged with the job of riding off across the countryside to announce the baby's safe arrival to all of the Colonel's neighbors.

After four sturdy sons, the Colonel was delighted to have a little girl to pet and pamper. Three more daughters arrived after Julia—Nellie, Mary, who died in childhood, and little Emma, the baby of the family. But Julia remained her father's favorite. He vowed she was the prettiest girl in Missouri and would one day be the belle of every ball.

Ellen Dent was more realistic about her daughter's looks. Julia had fair skin and soft brown hair but she was not a great beauty. Her features were plain and one of her eyes turned inward. The servants swore that it had happened when Annie took her from her hot bath too quickly and brought her into a cold room, but Mrs. Dent pooh-poohed the old wives' tale. Julia's eyes had been crossed at birth.

Ellen Dent did not set much store by good looks anyway. "There are other things that will serve a girl much better," she used to remind her husband, "like common sense and a good disposition."

The Colonel agreed. "But Julia has those, too," he insisted.

Mrs. Dent didn't contradict him.

Julia could be trusted to look after little Emma when Annie was busy in the kitchen and the only time she was ever cross was when her brothers pulled her braids and teased her about being too small to ride a horse. Then her chin would tremble and tears would brim in her large brown eyes. "I'm going to grow," she'd sob. "You'll see."

If Papa was home Julia would run off and beg him once more to let her take one of the horses and go riding across the meadows.

The Colonel found it hard to refuse her sorrowful entreaties. "But it's for your own safety," he would explain gently. "I don't want anything to happen to my little girl."

Occasionally he would swing Julia up in his own saddle and take her with him when he rode off to inspect his property and sometimes he let her ride behind her brother Fred, clinging to his waist as they trotted slowly down the road to school.

Julia had learned to read and write at the little log schoolhouse. She did not particularly like school but she enjoyed being with the boys and girls from the other farms in the neighborhood. Many of their parents were friends of her mother's and father's and she often saw them when they came to visit at White Haven.

The Dents liked to entertain. When they did, the dinner table would be set with Ellen Dent's best bone china and heavy English silver and the drawing room would be fragrant with the smell of fresh flowers. Julia and her sister Nellie liked to stand on the landing and peer over the black walnut banister at the ladies in their rustling silk and taffeta gowns, their hair shimmering in the candlelight.

The snatches of conversation that drifted up from downstairs were never particularly interesting to Julia. She could usually hear her father arguing about politics with his friend John O'Fallon or telling some of his other guests why Andrew Jackson was the best President the country ever had. Sometimes he would launch into one of his fiery denunciations of the abolitionists who were trying to do away with slavery.

Ellen and Frederick Dent were Southerners by birth. They had moved to Missouri soon after their marriage, but they had not forgotten their Maryland heritage. Frederick Dent adopted the courtesy title, Colonel, bought slaves to till his lands and run his house, and named his home White Haven after the family plantation he had known as a boy.

Julia did not know very much about slavery but if Papa said it was all right, she was willing to trust his judgment. Her main interest in lingering on the staircase was not to eavesdrop on the men's conversation but to listen when her father's cousin, John O'Fallon's pretty young wife, Caroline, played the piano. For a few moments, Julia would forget all about riding horses and climbing trees. She wanted only to learn to sing and play as sweetly as Cousin Caroline.

Ellen and Frederick Dent had no intention of letting Julia remain a tomboy all her life. The following September she was to begin studying at the Misses Moreau's classes in St. Louis.

Papa called her into his study one morning to talk

about it. "Now that you're ten," he said, peering at her over the tip of his white clay churchwarden's pipe, "I think it's high time you became an educated young lady."

At the Misses Moreau's classes, he explained, she would be able to study history and French and singing and art. If she wanted to, she could even learn to play the piano, like Cousin Caroline.

Julia was not surprised to learn that her father expected her to have more education than the log schoolhouse had to offer. Her brothers had spent only a few years there before going off to St. Louis to learn Latin and Greek at the boys' academy.

Colonel Dent was a firm believer in schooling. "A good mind is like a good horse," he used to say, "worth more when it's properly trained."

Although Julia had no objections to going to the Misses Moreau's School, her father launched into a lecture about education anyway. Julia had heard most of what he had to say before. She shifted uneasily from one small foot to the other. Her father's bushy eyebrows danced up and down on his forehead and he pointed his long pipe at her when he wanted to emphasize a particular point.

Not even Mrs. Dent would dare interrupt her husband when he was talking about one of his favorite subjects, but Julia was not afraid of her father's prickly disposition. "Papa," she burst out, "I want to ask you something."

The Colonel's eyebrows shot up in surprise. "What is it?" he said gruffly.

"If I'm big enough to go to a young ladies' seminary," Julia replied coolly, "it seems to me I'm big enough to learn to ride."

Colonel Dent pondered his daughter's proposition for a minute. Then he nodded gravely and said, "You're right."

With that, the Colonel took Julia's hand in his own and marched straight out of the house, down the front steps and around to the stables. "Jeff," he called to the groom, "saddle up the chestnut mare. Miss Julia's going to learn to ride."

A few minutes later, Jeff brought out the big brown horse and the Colonel lifted Julia up on her back. That first morning she did nothing but learn to hold the reins properly and sit straight in the saddle, but the next day, she was riding in an easy trot around the stable yard. By the middle of summer, Julia was so much at home on horseback that her father agreed to let her ride as fast and as far as she liked.

She was up before breakfast each morning, cantering across the open fields, her cheeks rosy from the cool morning air, her long braids flying behind her in the breeze. After that Colonel Dent was prouder than ever of his oldest daughter. "She's a born horsewoman," he beamed.

Even the boys had to admit that, despite her size, their sister had turned out to be a first rate rider "—for a girl," Fred added with a grin.

Fred, who was sixteen, prided himself on being the best horseman in the family. He wanted to go to West Point and become a lieutenant in the U.S. Cavalry. Then he would be as dashing as the officers he rode over to watch on the parade ground at Jefferson Barracks.

Now that Julia knew how to ride, he promised to take her over to the army post some afternoon. "And when I get to be a general," he told her, "I'll let you ride beside me to inspect the troops."

Julia frowned. "By then you'll have a wife," she said, "and you won't care about me at all."

"And you'll have a husband," Fred predicted, "somebody big, and tall, and rich, and handsome. . . ."

Julia couldn't imagine herself with a husband but she knew if she did have one, he would have to be more than that.

"You forgot the most important thing," she reminded Fred quickly. "He'll have to like horses, too."

II

WHEN THE DENTS stayed at their house in St. Louis, Nellie and Julia often took Emma down to the levee to watch the paddlewheel steamboats that sailed up and down the Mississippi. Julia thought they looked like a squadron of oversized ducks, gliding primly through the dark brown water. There were skiffs and flatboats on the river too, carrying cargoes that ranged from hogs and beaver pelts to families traveling westward.

The westbound travelers were everywhere in St. Louis, Their high canvas-covered wagons rattled along the cobblestone streets and when Julia went marketing with Mary Robinson, she saw women in homespun dresses and poke bonnets buying slabs of salt pork and sacks of coffee to feed their families on the long trek across the continent.

Julia soon got used to the pioneers, but she found it hard not to stare at some of the other people she saw in the busy port. There were long-haired trappers in leather jackets and coonskin caps, Indians in moccasins and bright colored beads, swarthy Mexicans, burly Germans, and Frenchmen descended from the settlers who had founded the city forty years before the Louisiana Purchase made it part of the United States.

Julia's new school was run by a pair of spinster sisters.

The classes were small and instead of being held in a regular school building, they met at the Misses Moreau's home in a residential section of St. Louis a few blocks up from the river.

The Dents lived close enough so Julia could walk to school. She was usually accompanied by Black Julia, the slave her father had given her when she was a baby. Several of the girls at the Misses Moreau's were shocked to discover that the Dents owned slaves. "My father thinks slavery is evil," one of Julia's classmates told her. "He says there ought to be a law against it."

When Julia asked her father about it at dinner that evening, he glowered at her from beneath his shaggy eyebrows. "The Dents have always owned slaves," he said grumpily, "and we've always taken good care of them. Now let's not have any more of that ridiculous talk at the dinner table."

At the Misses Moreau's School, Julia chose her own courses; she studied English composition, mythology, music, drawing, and needlework. Once a week, a dancing master came in to teach the girls gavottes and reels. The Misses Moreau also paid special attention to manners. Their pupils were expected to curtsy whenever one of their teachers addressed them and to say "please," "thank you" and "excuse me" even when they were only talking to each other at recess.

Julia's brother, Fred, pretended to be horrified at such niceties and accused his sister of turning into a young lady right before his eyes. "Don't worry," Julia giggled, "I'll never get too prim and proper to ride a horse."

When the Dents moved back to White Haven in the spring, Colonel Dent presented his daughter with a sleek black mare. The horse was a thoroughbred from one of

Kentucky's finest stables but Julia, out of loyalty to her home state, named her Missouri Belle.

Everyone in the family came out on the veranda to admire the new mount, and when Colonel Dent boosted Julia into the saddle for her first ride she glanced over at Fred and said, "What do you suppose the Misses Moreau would say if they could see me now?"

For as long as anyone in the family could remember, Fred had been talking about going to West Point. When he received his appointment in the spring of 1839, his shouts of joy could be heard all over the house. He hugged Julia and Nellie and whirled Emma around the room. "Hooray," he cried, "I'm off to join the army!"

The military academy was a thousand miles across the country in New York State. To get there, Fred had to travel by boat, stagecoach, and train. "It was an awful trip," he wrote home, "but the life of plebe is even worse. We have to get up at five in the morning and drill until our feet are ready to fall off on the parade ground."

His letter made Julia glad she was a girl and would never have to endure the life of a soldier.

Thanks to the Misses Moreau's lessons and her mother's insistence on daily practicing, Julia soon became an accomplished pianist. She sang too, and Colonel Dent, with his usual partiality, insisted that her voice was sweeter and clearer than Cousin Caroline O'Fallon's.

Like Colonel Dent, Caroline O'Fallon had been born in Maryland. She had been one of the prettiest belles in Baltimore before she married her banker husband and became one of the leaders of St. Louis society.

The O'Fallons were extremely fond of Julia. Cousin Caroline bought her gowns and silk bonnets and showed her how to dress her hair in the latest style. She also insisted that Julia regard the O'Fallons' mansion as her second home.

Julia was wide-eyed every time she visited the lovely house. Handsome oil paintings and finely carved statues adorned each room, and the furniture—delicate tables and graceful chairs upholstered in rich silk—had been imported from France. Julia sometimes wished that she could spend the rest of her life in such beautiful surroundings.

Julia graduated from the Misses Moreau's School in 1843. Two weeks later, Fred received his diploma from West Point and was commissioned a lieutenant in the United States Army. He had a few weeks' leave before reporting for duty and he came back to White Haven to spend it with his family.

Julia was glad to have her favorite brother home again. He regaled them with stories of some of the escapades he and his fellow cadets had been involved in at West Point. Sometimes they stole food from the mess hall and smuggled it out under their high leather hats. They also liked to sneak off the post at night and dash down to Benny Havens' tavern for a cup of hot toddy.

Julia noticed that Fred's roommate, Ulysses Grant, cropped up again and again in his stories, although Fred usually referred to him as Sam. "Tell us about Sam Grant," Nellie asked him one night. "Is he handsome?"

Fred grinned. "I don't know if he's handsome," he said. "But he sure can ride a horse. He was one of the few men at the Academy who could handle York."

"Who's York?" Emma demanded.

"A big sorrel stallion that was one of the meanest, toughest mounts in the stables," Fred explained. "The boys used to tell Sam that horse was going to kill him someday. But he'd ride him anyway. 'I can't die but once,' he used to say."

"And York didn't kill him?" Emma asked.

Fred shook his head, "Sam knew how to handle him," he said. "He set the Academy high-jump record on York . . . made that horse leap over a bar almost six feet high."

Even Colonel Dent was impressed with the feat. "Sam Grant sounds like quite a horseman," he said. "I'd like to shake his hand someday."

"You will," Fred promised. "There's a chance he'll be assigned to Jefferson Barracks. I told him to be sure and visit White Haven if he is."

Julia had hoped that Fred would be stationed at Jefferson Barracks but his regiment was ordered west instead. He gave each of his sisters a farewell kiss and warned them not to dare get married until he could get back to White Haven for the wedding.

"You don't have to worry about Emma and me," Nellie told him, "but we can't be sure about Julia."

At seventeen, Julia had developed into a remarkably pretty young lady. She was still tiny—just under five feet tall—and her fair complexion and ready smile always made people forget about her crossed eye. One or two young men had already come calling at White Haven and when winter came and the social season started in St. Louis, she was out every night at a different party. Colonel Dent grumbled that he hardly saw Julia anymore but his wife reminded him that he had predicted she'd be the belle of every ball. "Now you're complaining because she is," she said.

The Dents usually spent their winters in town and moved out to White Haven in the spring. Julia always looked forward to the move, but this year she was reluctant to leave St. Louis. "I'll miss too many parties," she told her mother. "Let me stay behind with Cousin Caroline."

Mrs. Dent gave in with a smile. "But I should think you'd be tired of dancing by now," she said.

"I'll never get tired of dancing," Julia replied emphatically.

For the next few weeks, Julia was involved in an incessant round of supper parties and cotillions. She was having such a good time that she hardly noticed when one of her partners suddenly became more attentive than the others. It was not until he started calling on her with boxes of chocolates and bunches of Parma violets that Julia began to get worried. "I don't want a serious beau," she told Cousin Caroline in alarm. "What am I going to do?"

Cousin Caroline had the perfect solution. "Go back to White Haven," she advised. "He'll soon forget all about you."

Two hours later, the O'Fallon carriage deposited Julia on the familiar pillared veranda, and Colonel Dent rushed out to embrace her. "It's about time you came home," he thundered good-naturedly. "I've been lonesome without you."

III

Emma and Nellie were eager to hear about the good times Julia had been having in St. Louis but they were equally anxious to bring her up-to-date on the happenings at White Haven.

"Fred's roommate, Ulysses Grant, is stationed at Jefferson Barracks," Nellie reported breathlessly. "Emma's got a crush on him."

The six-year-old blushed furiously. "I'm not the only one," she snapped. "You make a fuss over him, too."

The two girls told Julia how the youthful lieutenant had come riding up to the stile a few weeks earlier and spied Emma playing on the lawn. "How do you do, little girl," he said to her. "Does Mr. Dent live here?"

Emma took one look at the slim dark-haired officer and decided he looked like a dashing prince straight out of a book of fairy tales. She invited him to hitch his horse at the stile, and then she led him up to the front door where he introduced himself to Mrs. Dent.

With two of her sons away—George, married, and Fred, out west with the army—Mrs. Dent was happy to have another young man to fuss over. She insisted that Lieutenant Grant stay for supper and when he was leaving made him promise to return as soon as possible. Ulysses Grant took her at her word and since then he had been riding over to White Haven at least once a week.

He liked to chat with Nellie and to play with little Emma. More often, though, he sat in the library and discussed politics with Colonel Dent. The Colonel thought he was very intelligent. Mrs. Dent agreed. "That young man has a lot of sense," she told her family. "He'll be heard from someday."

Julia had been home for several days before Lieutenant Grant came calling again. When her mother summoned her into the parlor to meet him, she saw that he was just as good-looking as Emma had said. He was neither tall nor broad-shouldered but he had a square jaw and a fine straight nose. His eyes were amazingly blue and his dark brown hair was thick and wavy.

Julia offered him her hand. "I'm happy to meet you," she said pleasantly. "Fred's told us a lot about you."

The lieutenant greeted his roommate's favorite sister with a stiff, rather formal bow. He's shy, Julia thought. But later, when she studied him over the supper table, she realized that her first impression had been wrong. Ulysses Grant was not really shy—just thoughtful and quiet. Steady was the word Julia would have used if she had been asked to describe him.

The officers at Jefferson Barracks had to report for roll calls and drills. After that they were free to do whatever they wished. Ulysses Grant chose to spend more and more of his time at White Haven. The Dents were always pleased to see him. After supper in the evenings Julia would play the piano and sing, and Nellie would strum her guitar. Although their visitor listened politely, the girls soon discovered that he had no ear for music and was more at home on horseback than he was in a drawing room.

When he stayed overnight at White Haven, as Mrs. Dent so often urged him to, he and Julia would be out riding most of the day. Emma pouted because she was too young to go along; Nellie, too, was left behind. Only Missouri Belle could keep up with the long-legged stallion Lieutenant Grant had brought with him from Ohio.

One afternoon Ulysses and Julia were riding along a path through the woods when they heard a sharp cry of distress. Ulysses immediately charged off in the direction of the sound with Julia right behind him. They galloped into a small clearing and found a black man lying on the ground, his face contorted with pain.

It was one of Colonel Dent's slaves. He had been chopping wood when the axe slipped and cut a deep gash in his foot. Lieutenant Grant leaped out of his saddle and rushed to the man's assistance. He managed to stop most of the bleeding with his handkerchief. Then while Julia kept her thumbs pressed against the severed artery, he made a poultice out of the bark of an oak tree and tied it in place with a piece of the injured man's vest.

The dressing was no sooner finished than the man's wife appeared in the clearing. As soon as she saw that her husband was all right, she began to fuss because his rescuers had ripped up his vest. "Don't worry," Ulysses told her, "I'll buy him a new one."

He lifted the wounded man onto his horse and took him back to his cabin. "I'll stop by tomorrow to see how he is," he told Julia. "Right now, I have to be back at the Barracks for a dress parade."

The next day, Ulysses Grant appeared at the cabin door with the new vest under his arm. He had also brought along the regimental surgeon to dress the black man's wound. Julia arrived a few minutes later with a large smoked ham and several loaves of Mary Robinson's cornbread.

The wound was thoroughly washed and bandaged and the doctor assured the man that it would heal with no difficulty. He commended Ulysses and Julia for coming to his aid so promptly. "You should have been a doctor instead of a soldier," he told the lieutenant. "And Miss Dent," he said with a wink at Julia, "has a very cool head for a young lady. She ought to join the army."

Everyone at White Haven took the friendship between Ulysses and Julia for granted. Only Emma, who felt she had a special claim on the officer because she had seen him first, suspected that their relationship was something deeper than friendship.

When Ulysses Grant stayed overnight at White Haven, he usually lifted Emma up on his horse in the morning and gave her a ride to school. One day as they were approaching the log schoolhouse, he said playfully, "Look, Emmy, everyone in the schoolyard is watching us. They're saying 'There's Emmy Dent! She's got her sweetheart with her.' "

Emma's eyes blazed. "More like my sister's sweetheart!" she retorted as she slipped out of the saddle and raced towards the schoolhouse door.

Ulysses dismissed Emma's remark. He had other things on his mind that April morning. There was a strong possibility that the United States would soon be at war with Mexico. If that happened, his regiment was certain to be called into action.

The United States and her southern neighbor were quarreling over Texas. The future state had declared its independence from Mexico a few years before and was now a separate republic. President John Tyler wanted to annex it to the United States but Mexico objected to the annexation and even in the United States there was a sharp difference of opinion about the move.

The Democrats, mostly Southerners like Colonel Dent, thought annexation was a good idea. The Northerners, who were mainly Republicans, were violently opposed to the plan. They said the United States had no right to take over another country, but that was not the only reason for their stand. They were also afraid that the annexed land would be used for the extension of slavery.

Ulysses Grant sided with the northerners and he was not afraid to say so. He stood his ground even when Colonel Dent shouted and pounded the table and called the Republicans "a pack of fools and ninnies."

"I know you don't agree with me, sir," Ulysses said calmly, "but I think we ought to leave Texas alone."

Julia had always accepted her father's opinions without question, but as she listened to Lieutenant Grant she began to realize that many of the things he was saying made sense. Maybe Papa wasn't always right after all.

If the United States annexed Texas, a war with Mexico was inevitable. Ulysses Grant decided to apply for twenty days' leave to go back to Ohio to visit his family. "If war is declared," he told the Dents, "this will be my last chance to see them for a long while." On May first, he boarded the steamboat to Cincinnati. From there it was only twelve miles to his home town of Bethel.

The Grants had not seen their son since his graduation from West Point. He had been sick with the ague during his last months at the military academy and his weight had dropped to a mere 117 pounds. Since he had been at Jefferson Barracks, however, he had gained at least twenty-five pounds and his father and mother both commented on how well he looked. Ulysses told them about his visits to White Haven and remarked, "It must be Mary Robinson's good cooking."

Hannah and Jesse Grant were furious to learn that their son had been visiting in the home of a slave owner. "You know how your mother and I feel about slavery," Jesse Grant said.

"And you know I agree with you," Ulysses replied, "but the Dents are fine people and I don't see anything wrong with accepting their hospitality."

Ulysses had been looking forward to his visit to Ohio but after a few days at home, he began to grow restless. At first he wondered how he could possibly be lonesome for an army barracks but the more he thought about it, the more he realized it wasn't Jefferson Barracks he missed, it was White Haven.

Julia Dent's face kept appearing in his thoughts. He remembered her sweet voice and her happy smile and the way her brown hair shone in the sunlight. Although he went riding every day in Bethel, it was not as much fun without Julia on Missouri Belle beside him. It seemed strange to come upon a field of daisies and not stop and pick one for her to wear in her hair.

Half of Ulysses' twenty-day leave had passed when he suddenly announced that he had to return to St. Louis. His baffled father drove the lovesick lieutenant to the steamboat and he was back at Jefferson Barracks by the end of the week.

Stopping only to report to his commanding officer, Ulysses put on a fresh uniform, saddled his horse and galloped off in the direction of White Haven. Less than a mile from the house he encountered an unexpected obstacle.

A small creek meandered through part of the trail. Ordinarily, it was no more than a sliver of water but heavy spring rains had filled the creek bed to overflowing and the narrow stream had turned into an angry torrent. Ulysses saw at once that it had become a treacherous crossing. The swollen waters were way above his head and the current was so strong it could easily sweep both him and his horse downstream.

Caution dictated a return to Jefferson Barracks but Ulysses ignored it and plunged into the raging torrent. After a desperate struggle against the onrushing current, he emerged at last on the opposite bank, safe but completely drenched.

Nellie Dent could not help giggling when he came riding up to the stile at White Haven. His freshly pressed uniform had turned into a sopping mass of dark blue cloth and his boots sloshed when he dismounted. When Nellie led him into the front hall and he saw himself in the mirror, Ulysses was forced to laugh, too.

Julia's brother John offered to lend him some dry clothes but when he came downstairs a few minutes later, there were even more peals of laughter. John was taller and heavier than Ulysses. The shoulders on his suit coat drooped and the sleeves had to be turned back almost to the elbow. "I'm afraid I look pretty silly," Ulysses said with a self-conscious smile.

"It doesn't matter," Mrs. Dent hastened to assure him. "We're glad to see you anyway."

Ulysses Grant stole a quick glance at Julia who was standing by her mother's side. He wanted to ask her if she was glad to see him too but he saw that he didn't have to. The smile in her dark brown eyes told him that she was.

IV

FOR THE NEXT FEW DAYS, Ulysses Grant was a constant visitor in the Dent household. He was practically a member of the family so it seemed perfectly natural for him to spend some time at White Haven before his leave was over. Unfortunately, everyone made such a fuss over him that he had no chance to be alone with the main reason for his return—Julia.

John Dent dragged him off to look at a horse he was thinking of buying from a farmer down the road. Emma insisted that he take her hunting for birds' nests and Colonel Dent cornered him in the library and demanded to know if he had changed his mind about annexing Texas.

When Ulysses told him, "No, sir," the Colonel's face furrowed into an angry scowl. "Now, Frederick," Mrs. Dent interrupted quickly, "Lieutenant Grant is entitled to his opinion just as you are entitled to yours."

Three days of his precious leave slipped away and Ulysses still hadn't told Julia that he loved her. He would ride back to Jefferson Barracks each evening and stare glumly at the calendar over his cot. "Tomorrow," he would promise himself. But the next day there would be another family dinner, another discussion with Colonel Dent, another romp with Emma—and still no chance to be alone with Julia.

On Saturday, Ulysses' luck finally changed. The Dents were invited to a wedding and Mrs. Dent asked him to come along. Julia's parents were driving to the church in one buggy; she and her brother John would follow in another. Lieutenant Grant could ride along beside them on his horse.

Colonel and Mrs. Dent drove off and John and Julia were left standing by the stile waiting for Ulysses to join them. Julia had on a pale pink dress with a bonnet to match. It set off her fair complexion and made a pleasing contrast to her dark brown hair and eyes. When Ulysses Grant arrived a few minutes later, he took one look at the pretty eighteen-year-old and knew that he could be silent no longer.

Jumping out of his saddle, he handed the reins to John. "Let's change places," he said. "You take my horse and I'll drive Julia in the buggy."

John was glad of a chance to ride the handsome stallion. He leaped into the saddle before Ulysses could change his mind and started off down the road. By the time Ulysses had climbed into the buggy, he was already out of sight.

The determined suitor made no effort to catch up with him. Instead he let the horse clop along at a sedate trot and listened to Julia chatting lightly about the balmy May weather. "It's so warm and sunny," she said. "Isn't it a perfect day for a wedding?"

Ulysses said nothing and for an instant Julia was tempted to ask him why he was in such a silent mood. She decided not to. He was probably worrying about the trouble with Mexico and it was much too nice a day to start talking about war.

The church where the wedding was being held was several miles from White Haven. To get there they had to cross a wooden bridge that stretched over a deep ravine. As Ulysses had discovered to his chagrin a few days before, heavy spring rains had swollen even the tiniest creeks in the area. The ravine, which was usually dry, had become still another avenue for the rushing waters. As the buggy approached the bridge, Julia was astonished to see the newly created river and even more astonished to see that its waters were so high, they were lapping over the wooden planks of the bridge.

"It's never been like this before," she said nervously. "Do you think it's safe to cross?"

Ulysses Grant pulled in the reins and studied the bridge for a minute. "What do you think?" Julia asked again.

He did not reply immediately and Julia wondered if he, too, was worried about the danger. "Maybe we should go back," she suggested. "There's another road that's a little bit longer but perhaps it would be better. . . ."

Ulysses shook his head. "It's a sturdy bridge," he said at last. His voice was so reassuring that Julia decided it was silly to worry.

Ulysses slapped the reins down on the horse's back and they started over the bridge. They had gone about halfway when Julia again looked down at the angry waters. A horrible vision suddenly danced before her eyes.

She could see the bridge being washed away and the horse and buggy swallowed up in the current. She could almost feel herself being dragged under, too, but she made a great effort to remain calm. Putting her hand on Ulysses' arm, she said in a faint voice, "If anything happens please let me hang on to you."

"All right," Ulysses replied. A few seconds later, they

were safely across the planks and Julia breathed a long sigh of relief. She looked over at Ulysses and wondered if he realized how frightened she had been, but his face was set in the same impassive mask he had worn all day.

"Maybe a wedding will cheer you up," she said impulsively.

"Yes," he said thoughtfully, "I think it would."

He looked at her strangely and then drew the buggy to a sudden halt by the side of the road. Turning to her with an uncertain smile, he reached for her hand. "A little while ago, you asked me if I would let you hang on to me if anything happened," he said. "I'd like to have you hang on to me forever."

The humor disappeared from his voice and his tone became quite serious. "Julia," he said, "will you be my wife?"

Julia had not been expecting his proposal but she wasn't the least bit startled when it came. She liked the idea of marrying this quiet, dark-haired man and it never occurred to her to tell him anything but yes.

The rest of the way to the wedding and all the way back, Julia and Ulysses laughed and talked as happily as a pair of school children. Julia said she had never suspected that Ulysses cared for her. "I never suspected it myself," he confessed. "In fact, if I hadn't gone home on leave, I might never have found out at all."

"I was sorry when you left," Julia admitted. "There wasn't anyone to go riding with."

It was not until after dinner that evening that the two lovers again had a chance to be alone. Ulysses invited Julia to take a stroll in the garden. They walked in silence until they reached the rose arbor. There he took her hand and asked her to set a date for their wedding.

Julia hesitated. "I . . . don't know what to say," she stammered. "You haven't talked to Papa yet."

Ulysses stared down at the tips of his shiny black boots. "I hate to admit this, Julia," he said, half joking but half in earnest too, "but I'd almost rather go off and get shot at by Mexicans than ask your father to let me marry you."

"I know," Julia sighed. "Father isn't going to approve of this at all. And you know he's not shy about saying what he thinks."

Ulysses thought Colonel Dent would object to him because he was a Northerner and a Republican. Julia knew there was another reason. Her father had often said that he would never let any of his daughters marry a soldier. Their pay was low, the living conditions on army posts were wretched and worst of all, they were always being shipped out west. Several of his friends' daughters had married West Pointers and the Colonel had seen firsthand what a difficult life it was.

Ulysses had been hoping that he and Julia could be married as soon as possible but Julia shook her head. "First we have to tell Papa we're engaged," she announced firmly. "Then we have to give him some time to get used to the idea."

In Washington, Congress was still arguing over President Tyler's request for the annexation of Texas. No one could be certain what the final vote would be but the army was making cautious preparations for war. Ulysses' regiment had been ordered out of Jefferson Barracks and sent to a camp in Louisiana that was closer to the Texas border. Ulysses, who had arrived back from Ohio to find them gone, would have to join them there when his leave expired.

After talking it over with Julia, the disappointed soldier agreed not to ask Colonel Dent for his daughter's hand right away. "Let's keep our engagement a secret for now," she said.

When Ulysses pointed out that the Colonel would have to be informed sooner or later, Julia came up with a plan. "Wait until you get to your new post," she suggested, "and then write him a letter."

Ulysses smiled wryly. "Even at that distance, I'll probably hear his cries of outrage when he reads it," he said.

On the final day of his leave, Ulysses rode back to White Haven to bid farewell to the Dents. Mrs. Dent gave him a motherly kiss and the Colonel, unaware of his marriage plans, shook his hand. "I don't approve of your politics," he said gruffly, "but I wish you godspeed just the same."

The rest of the Dents lined up on the veranda to wave good-bye to the departing officer. Only Nellie and Emma were missing and Julia took advantage of their absence to walk down to the stile alone with Ulysses.

"Don't lose your heart to someone else while I'm gone," he ordered her sternly as he climbed into the saddle.

Julia reached up and touched his hand lightly. "I won't," she told him with a smile. "You said I could hang on to you forever and that's exactly what I intend to do!"

V

Ulysses Grant took the riverboat from St. Louis down the Mississippi to New Orleans. From there he had to travel back up the river to Camp Salubrity. He found his regiment, the Fourth Infantry, already settled in their new quarters. A mess kitchen had been set up, a parade ground marked off, and neat rows of army tents were pitched in the once barren fields.

The camp sat on a sandy plateau in the middle of a forest of pine trees. It was hot and dusty and crawling with insects. Ulysses' bed was a wooden plank resting on four tree stumps. Before lying down at night, he had to shoo away ants, mosquitoes, ticks, and even an occasional scorpion. If it rained, he gave up all hope of sleep. The tent leaked and it was like lying in a shower bath.

On top of these discomforts, Ulysses was not looking forward to composing the letter he had promised to send to Colonel Dent. He rewrote it several times and finally, with deep misgivings, dropped it into the company mail sack. He never received an answer.

When the letter arrived at White Haven, Colonel Dent snorted and tossed it aside. "You're too young and that boy's too poor," he snapped when Julia asked him about it. "He hasn't anything to give you."

Julia's brown eyes flashed and she stamped her foot indignantly. "I'm poor, too," she snapped. "What have I got to give him?"

Colonel Dent was not a rich man. He owned two comfortable homes but he spent most of his income maintaining them. He might have been better off had he not insisted on running his Missouri farm like the Maryland plantation he had lived on as a boy. Housing and feeding slaves and their families cost more than paying servants to work.

The Colonel ignored his daughter's anger and flatly refused to answer her suitor's letter. "Don't worry, Miss Julia," Mary Robinson said when she saw her tears, "he'll come around after a while. He can't bear to refuse you anything."

If Colonel Dent had expected the six hundred miles between St. Louis and Camp Salubrity to cool the young couple's affection, he was greatly mistaken. Ulysses and Julia wrote to each other regularly and Julia let it be known that the young men who came calling at White Haven would have to pay court to her younger sister Nellie. Julia's heart belonged to somebody else.

Ulysses' letters from Louisiana described some of the rigors of life at Camp Salubrity. Even worse than the heat and the insects, he reported, was the lack of anything to do. The officers quickly got bored playing cards and racing each other on horseback. A few of them almost hoped that war would be declared against Mexico. It would at least get them away from Camp Salubrity.

Congress voted to annex Texas on March 1, 1845. The Mexicans immediately threatened to go to war. But James Polk, who had succeeded John Tyler in the White House, sent emissaries to talk to them. For several months it looked as if the differences between the two nations might be settled peacefully, but then the Mexicans changed their minds. When they refused to receive President Polk's representatives, the President ordered the army to start marching toward the Rio Grande. The long-awaited war against Mexico was about to begin.

Ulysses Grant considered the war a tragic mistake, but as an American soldier he felt honorbound to fight wherever his country sent him. He could not go off to battle, however, without one last visit with Julia. He even cherished a faint hope that Colonel Dent might agree to let them be married while he was home on leave.

With a three weeks' pass in his uniform pocket, Ulysses headed back to New Orleans and the steamboat to St. Louis. Julia's father was the first person he caught sight of when he came galloping up to White Haven a few days later.

The Colonel was out on the veranda getting ready to leave on a trip to Washington. His bags were already loaded onto the buggy that would take him to the steamboat and his wife and daughters were standing in the doorway stuffing shopping lists in his pocket to remind him of the new gloves and bolts of ribbon they wanted him to bring back from the capital.

Ulysses hitched his horse at the stile and strode up the path to the house. Julia caught her breath when she saw how much handsomer he looked. His skin was tanned from the Louisiana sun and he seemed to have grown stronger and firmer. He shook hands with Colonel Dent and said purposefully, "I'd like to talk to you for a moment, sir."

The Colonel cleared his throat and muttered something about being in a hurry to get off to Washington. But Mrs. Dent understood what was on the officer's mind. "There's no rush, Frederick," she told her husband. "You have a few minutes to spare."

With that she ushered the young man and the older one into the library and closed the double doors firmly behind them.

Lieutenant Grant wasted no time. "Julia and I want to be married," he said boldly.

To his amazement, Colonel Dent kept his temper. "You do, do you?" he replied calmly. "Well, now, I'll have to think about that."

It was encouraging but not as encouraging as Ulysses would have liked. His hopes for an immediate wedding sank still lower when the Colonel said, "Julia's barely nineteen. That's too young to be rushing into marriage."

Before Ulysses could say anything more the Colonel insisted that he had to be leaving or he'd miss his boat. He strode out of the library, kissed his wife and daughters good-bye, and started off for Washington.

Julia tried to be optimistic about the interview. "At least he didn't say no," she reminded Ulysses.

"But he didn't exactly say yes either," he replied morosely.

Ulysses was miserable at the prospect of a long engagement. His only consolation was that Mrs. Dent had invited him to stay at White Haven so he at least could see Julia every day.

When the weather was fair, they went riding. Sometimes they took along a picnic basket and stopped beside a brook to have their lunch. Ulysses usually had a book tucked away in his saddlebag and when they were finished eating he would read aloud for a while.

Julia liked his voice. It was low but firm, the kind of

voice you could respect and obey. She could imagine him giving orders to his men on the battlefield.

In the evening, Ulysses and Julia sat in the parlor and talked. Ulysses told her about his boyhood in Ohio and explained how his classmates at West Point had given him the nickname Sam.

"I was christened Hiram Ulysses Grant," he said, "but when I started to stencil my initials on my army trunk, I realized they spelled HUG."

Julia giggled.

"I switched them around to make it UHG," he went on, "but when I got to the academy, I lost the H completely. Someone had listed me on the roll as U.S. Grant. That started everyone calling me Uncle Sam and eventually it got shortened to Sam."

Julia found the story amusing but she knew she would never call her fiancé by his West Point nickname. As far as she was concerned, Ulysses sounded much nicer than plain old Sam.

One night, Ulysses and Julia drove into St. Louis to have dinner with the O'Fallons. John O'Fallon knew Ulysses' commanding officer, Zachary Taylor. He had served with him in the War of 1812 and the two men exchanged yarns about "Old Fuss and Feathers," as Taylor's troops called him. Ulysses also talked to Cousin Caroline about some cadets she knew from Baltimore who had been in his class at West Point.

Caroline O'Fallon liked his quiet humor and straightforward manner. When it was time for them to go home, she hugged her younger cousin and said, "Your lieutenant is much nicer than any of the other young men who used to call on you. I know you're going to be very happy."

Ulysses and Julia both dreaded the day when his leave would be over. When it finally came, they kissed good-bye in the garden and promised to write to each other as often as they could.

With Ulysses on his way back to his regiment, Julia, like a dutiful bride-to-be, settled down to hemstitching sheets and embroidering towels for their future home. She also began making a patchwork quilt. It was monotonous work sewing the small cotton squares together and Julia soon grew weary. After a few days, she put the quilt aside and started working on a new dress instead. "If you give up that easily," her mother admonished her, "you'll never finish it."

"Of course I'll finish it," Julia told her. "I'm just taking a little rest."

When the Dents were at White Haven, Julia never missed a chance for a canter on Missouri Belle. Wherever she rode, she was reminded of Ulysses. There were few trails they had not explored together, few meadows where they had not picnicked or gathered wildflowers. In St. Louis, she was not quite as lonesome. There she could shop or go visiting or join Cousin Caroline for a drive in Lafayette Park.

Soon after Ulysses returned to Louisiana, the Fourth Infantry pulled up stakes at Camp Salubrity and started marching toward the Mexican border. The actual fighting began in April and by the middle of May when war was officially declared, Ulysses' regiment had already been in two engagements.

It was his first taste of combat and he was pleasantly surprised to find that he was not afraid. In one skirmish, a Mexican shell had burst only a few feet away from him, he wrote back to Julia, and though he had been showered with dirt, he had not been harmed. He was hoping his good luck would continue.

Julia had been reading about the fighting in the newspapers for several weeks before Ulysses' letter arrived. She rushed to her writing table and wrote a letter of her own telling him how much she loved him and how she wished they had been married before he went off to war. "Please come home safely," she wrote, ". . . and soon."

The fighting dragged on. Julia followed every step of the army's weary progress in the newspapers and soon knew almost as much about Mexico as she did about Missouri. The Americans were winning most of the battles but the casualty lists were long and heartbreaking to read. Several officers who had been stationed at Jefferson Barracks with Ulysses were already among the dead.

The Dents had a double reason to be anxious. Soon after the Fourth Infantry left for Mexico, Fred's regiment was also ordered into action. For weeks no news arrived at White Haven from either of the two officers. Then one day a hastily dashed-off note from Ulysses informed Colonel and Mrs. Dent that their son had been hit in the thigh by a musketball during the battle of Molino del Rey. Fred was now in an army hospital, Ulysses said, and seemed none the worse for his wound.

A week later, a letter from Fred confirmed the story and added a few more details. Colonel Dent read it aloud to his family. Fred's company had stormed an abandoned mill that was serving as a garrison for some Mexican soldiers. Sam Grant was leading the second wave of attackers and when he entered the mill he found Fred lying on the ground, blood streaming from his leg.

With the battle raging on all sides of him, Sam stopped to bind up Fred's wound and carry him to safety. "If it wasn't for Sam," Fred wrote, "I wouldn't be alive to write this letter."

By the time Colonel Dent got to the last line of the letter, Mrs. Dent was wiping tears of relief from her eyes. Nellie and Julia were speechless, but Emma spoke up at once. "Well, Papa," she declared triumphantly, "you can't stop Ulysses from marrying Julia now. He saved Fred's life."

The Colonel furrowed his bushy eyebrows and seemed about to send her to her room for her impudence. Then he thought better of it and said with a broad smile, "Julia and Lieutenant Grant have my permission to get married the instant he gets back from Mexico."

VI

THE WAR ENDED in the fall of 1847, but the Fourth Infantry remained on duty in Mexico for several months after the peace treaty was signed. It was not until July of 1848 that Ulysses at last made his way back to White Haven.

He had been gone for over two years but if anything, his love for Julia had grown stronger. He was glad to see that she felt the same way. When he swept her into his arms and asked her how soon they could be married, her dark eyes glowed with joy and she laughed exuberantly and replied, "Right away."

Julia got out the calendar and selected August twenty-second as the best date. "I wish it could be even sooner," she sighed, "but you have to give me some time to pick out a wedding dress."

For awhile they considered being married at White Haven but Julia thought town weddings were more fashionable. "What do you think, Ulysses?" she asked her fiancé.

Ulysses shrugged. "I don't know anything about fashion," he said good-naturedly. "You'd better ask Nellie or Emma."

It was Mrs. Dent who made the final decision. "The town house is more convenient," she said. "Nobody wants to drive out to White Haven in the summer heat."

Towards the end of July the Dents moved into St. Louis to get ready for the big day. Mary Robinson saw to it that every stick of furniture in the brick town house was polished with fragrant lemon oil and each cut glass droplet on the chandeliers was lovingly washed in warm sudsy water.

While the black women were busy getting the house in order, Julia and Nellie helped Mrs. Dent draw up the guest list and send out the wedding invitations. Most of the bride-to-be's time, however, was taken up with parties. "Everyone in St. Louis wants to meet you," she told Ulysses.

Two of her bridesmaids gave dinners for the engaged couple and Caroline and John O'Fallon gave a splendid ball. Julia wore a gown of pale green organdy with a low-cut neck and a wide hoop skirt. She had a pair of satin slippers to match and her brown hair was swept back and twisted into a fat chignon.

"Isn't this fun?" she said, beaming at Ulysses as they whirled around the dance floor. She knew from his half-hearted smile that he would rather be somewhere else. He was too quiet and thoughtful for the frivolous chatter of the ballroom.

Ulysses and Julia had agreed to spend their honeymoon visiting his parents in Bethel, Ohio. But Ulysses wanted to return home before that to tell them in person about his forthcoming marriage. With the wedding less than three weeks away, he decided to make the journey back to Bethel alone.

"Look at that," Jesse Grant exclaimed the instant he caught sight of the ribbons on his son's chest. "You've won a medal."

Ulysses had been decorated for bravery in Mexico and his proud father lost no time in bragging about it to the neighbors. Hannah Grant, Ulysses' mother, was more reserved than her husband. She gave her son a perfunctory smile and said quietly, "It's good to have you back."

It was not a very warm reception, but Ulysses was used to his mother's unemotional nature. She rarely laughed or raised her voice in anger and he had yet to see her shed a tear.

Although he had hinted at a forthcoming marriage in his letters, Ulysses' parents were startled to hear that the wedding was to take place so soon. They were even more disturbed at the idea of their son marrying into a family that kept slaves.

Ulysses urged his parents to come up to St. Louis for the wedding but they declined. "We're plain folks," Jesse Grant said sullenly. "We'd feel out of place with all that southern fuss and finery."

When Ulysses arrived back in Missouri, the plans for the wedding were well under way. Caroline O'Fallon had insisted on buying Julia her wedding gown. Julia said it was the most beautiful dress she had ever seen, but when Ulysses asked if he could have a look at it, she shook her head emphatically. "Of course not," she said. "It's bad luck."

It was also supposed to be bad luck for the bride and groom to see each other before the wedding but Ulysses refused to pay attention to superstitions. With the ceremony scheduled for eight that evening, he came around to call on Julia at three in the afternoon.

Emma answered the door. "Go away," she told him. "You're not supposed to be here yet."

Ulysses grinned. "I'm not afraid of bad luck," he replied. "Run upstairs and tell Julia that she shouldn't be either."

Emma had no sooner delivered the message than her sister came dashing downstairs. She sat on the front steps talking to Ulysses until Mrs. Dent finally had to send Black Julia down to remind her that she was being married that evening and it might be a good idea if she came inside and helped with the packing for her honeymoon.

A few hours later, Julia stood at the top of the long staircase waiting for the musicians in the parlor to strike up the wedding march. Her dress of white silk was trimmed with delicate bands of lace and her veil was held in place with tiny sprigs of white flowers.

Colonel Dent kissed his daughter lightly through her filmy veil before offering her his arm. "That soldier boy's been waiting for four years," he whispered as they started down the stairs. "Let's not keep him a minute longer."

The pastor of the Dents' church performed the simple ceremony. It took less than fifteen minutes. Ulysses and Julia each repeated the marriage vows. Then Ulysses slipped a narrow gold band on his bride's tiny finger and the minister pronounced them man and wife.

Ulysses was the first to kiss the bride. His best man, Captain James Longstreet, was next. "Pete," as he was called, had been married himself only a few months before. His wife Louise squeezed Julia's hand. "I hope you'll be as happy as we are," she murmured.

The wedding guests toasted the newlyweds in champagne and feasted by candlelight in the flower-banked dining room. Emma, the youngest of the merrrymakers, also seemed to be having the best time. She ate three pieces of Mary Robinson's white tiered wedding cake and

stepped on everybody's toes trying to keep up with the bride and groom as they made their way around the room shaking hands with their friends.

"Emma, I'm glad I married Julia instead of you," Ulysses told her with a smile. "You're an awful pest."

All the brides that Julia knew received pearls or diamond brooches as wedding gifts from their husbands. Ulysses Grant had no money to spend on expensive jewelry. His gift to Julia was a picture of himself encased in a small gold locket. She wore it on a velvet wrist strap when they left for Ohio the next day.

"Isn't this wonderful!" Julia exclaimed as they stood on the upper deck watching the paddlewheel steamer nudge its way out of the dock and head downstream to the Ohio River.

It was Julia's first trip on a riverboat and she found it a marvelous adventure. She loved to sit by their stateroom window at night and gaze at the lights twinkling along the shore. In the dining room she became so engrossed in the scenery gliding by that she almost forgot to eat her meals.

As the boat drew closer to Ohio, however, Julia began to worry. "Do you think your mother and father will approve of me?" she asked Ulysses anxiously.

"Why shouldn't they?" he replied.

When Julia still looked worried, he patted her hand reassuringly. "Of course they'll like you," he said. "How can they help it?"

Ulysses had told Julia all about his family. There were six children in all—two more boys and three girls. The youngest, Mary Frances, was only nine years old. His own favorite was sixteen-year-old Virginia. "She's the beauty of the family," he said.

Ulysses' father owned a leather factory and the Grants

lived in a brick house only a few doors away from it. Julia could not help feeling nervous as Ulysses pushed open the front door and showed her into the parlor. She was wearing a striped silk dress that she had selected especially for the occasion. She soon realized, however, that Hannah Grant was not impressed by stylish clothes. Her one good dress was plain black and the only trim was a white kerchief at the throat.

Mrs. Grant greeted her new daughter-in-law with only a faint trace of a smile. Jesse Grant was, as usual, more outgoing. "Sit down," he urged Julia. "We're glad to meet the young lady who's finally snagged our son."

The rest of the Grant family trooped in to shake hands and stare at their brother's wife. They seemed to approve of her and even Hannah Grant grew friendlier when at dinner time Julia covered her silk dress with an apron and came out in the kitchen to mash the potatoes.

Jesse Grant tasted them and gave Julia a nod of approval. "I thought you southern belles didn't spend much time doing housework," he remarked in surprise.

"My sisters and I were all taught to cook and keep house," Julia informed him politely. "My mother insisted on it."

Julia and Ulysses spent almost three weeks in Bethel. They went riding in the woods where Ulysses had played as a boy and strolled along the creek where he had learned to swim. Everyone in town made a fuss over them. The women admired Julia's stylish clothes and the men wanted to hear every detail of Ulysses' adventures in Mexico.

Although she found it hard to express her feelings, Hannah Grant seemed to approve of her son's wife. Jesse liked her, too. He lectured her endlessly on politics and even invited her down to his tannery to see how leather was made.

Julia made an effort to act interested in the long racks of hides. She asked polite questions about tanning and tried to ignore the foul odor that permeated the busy factory.

Ulysses, who was with her, made no attempt to disguise his distaste for the place. He had worked there for a while before going to West Point. "After two weeks," he told Julia, "I was willing to do anything to get out of there."

He had originally thought of becoming a farmer but what he had really wanted was a good education. It was that, more than a love for the military life, which had prompted him to apply to the military academy.

When it was time for Ulysses and Julia to return to St. Louis, Jesse and Hannah Grant came to the steamboat landing in Cincinnati to see them off. Jesse made Julia promise to come visit them again, and his wife nodded her agreement.

As they stood on the top deck of the steamer waving good-bye, the young bride squeezed her husband's arm. "I like all the Grants," she said impulsively, "especially you."

"And all the Grants like you," Ulysses replied, "especially me."

VII

DURING HIS TWO YEARS of service in Mexico, Ulysses had accumulated over three months' leave. The newlyweds returned from Ohio in September and decided to spend their last weeks of freedom at White Haven. "We'll go riding every day," Julia said, adding with a mischievous smile, "and at night you and Papa can argue about William Lloyd Garrison."

William Lloyd Garrison was a Boston newspaper editor who was dedicated to the abolition of slavery. Everytime his name was mentioned in Colonel Dent's presence, he turned purple with rage.

Ulysses laughed and told Julia that he planned to ignore her suggestion. "Your father's finally beginning to like me," he said. "Let's not spoil it by bringing up the subject of slavery."

Slavery had been a bone of contention between Northerners and Southerners for as long as Julia could remember. It was a particularly lively issue at the moment because the Mexican War had given the United States vast territories in the west. A group of Northerners in Congress had already called for the exclusion of slavery in the states that were carved out of these new lands. The Southerners defeated the measure but passions were aroused on both sides of the question. In the north, the abolitionists began calling for the emancipation of all slaves. In the south, there was talk of settling the argument by seceding from the union and forming a separate confederacy of states.

The Northerners and the Southerners each stood so firm in their views that Julia could not help wondering how the slavery question would ever be settled. When she asked Ulysses, he shook his head. "All I know," he said darkly, "is that if it isn't settled, it's going to end up tearing this country apart."

Although his own sentiments lay firmly with the north, Ulysses gingerly sidestepped the subject of slavery every time Colonel Dent tried to broach it at the dinner table. When Julia playfully accused him of being a coward, he readily admitted it. "Of course I'm a coward," he said cheerfully. "It's the only way to keep peace in the family."

The Missouri weather was sunny and clear that fall. Ulysses and Julia went riding and picnicking as they had done on so many spring days during their courtship. Now, however, the paths were strewn with fallen leaves and there was a hint of winter in the wind.

"I wonder where we'll be next month at this time," Julia mused as they were riding home through the woods one afternoon.

"We'll soon find out," Ulysses replied. "My orders are probably in the mail right now."

He had already learned that the Fourth Infantry was being divided into a number of smaller companies and deployed to a string of forts along the Canadian border. He had reason to believe, however, that his own assignment would be the regimental headquarters in Detroit. "I hope so," Julia said when he mentioned it to her. "Papa can't complain about that."

Colonel Dent had been in a surprisingly benevolent

mood towards his new son-in-law but as Ulysses' leave began to run out, he started brooding about where his favorite daughter was going to live. "Don't worry, Papa," Julia told him. "I'm sure it will be someplace civilized."

"Civilized!" her father grunted contemptuously. "There's no such thing as a civilized army post. They're all out in the middle of nowhere."

The remark proved to be something of a prophecy. Ulysses' orders, which arrived a few days later, called for him to report not to Detroit, but to Madison Barracks in Sackett's Harbor, New York.

Julia could tell by the set of her husband's jawline that he was disappointed at the news. "I've never been to New York," she said, trying to look on the bright side of the assignment. "This will be a new adventure."

Ulysses gave her a skeptical smile. "Do you have any idea where Sackett's Harbor is?" he said.

He went into the library, took her father's atlas down from one of the shelves and flipped to the map of New York State. "There," he said pointing to a small dot along the edge of Lake Ontario. "It doesn't look like a very good place to spend the winter, does it?"

Julia shivered when she saw how far north it was. "I'll bring plenty of warm clothes, and lots of heavy blankets," she said with a determined smile. "And maybe I'll even finish the quilt I started while you were in Mexico."

When Ulysses broke the news to Colonel Dent of where they would be living, he reacted exactly as they had anticipated. "You can't take Julia up there," he fumed. "She'll die of double pneumonia."

Before Ulysses could reply, Ellen Dent spoke up. "Julia's not as frail as she looks," she reminded her husband. "I'm sure she'll be all right."

"Of course she'll be all right," Nellie chimed in, "and

besides I'm sure she'd rather risk pneumonia and be with Ulysses than die of loneliness here at home."

Julia nodded her emphatic agreement and Colonel Dent finally threw up his hands in despair. "All right. Go ahead," he cried, "but if you come down with double pneumonia, don't say I didn't warn you."

Sackett's Harbor was just as cold and bleak as Ulysses had feared. Madison Barracks consisted of a group of block houses that had been built along Lake Ontario during the War of 1812. Behind them were the rows of wooden cabins that housed the officers and their wives. The one that was assigned to the Grants looked exactly like all the rest—a boxlike structure with dull brown walls and splintery floors. What startled Julia most of all, though, was its size. All four rooms could have fit into the parlor at White Haven.

"Do you think you can make it livable?" Ulysses asked anxiously.

Julia did not reply at once. Instead she walked slowly around the little house studying the rooms more closely. The bedroom and dining room were already furnished. That left only the parlor to worry about.

She was already decorating it in her imagination. A black horsehair sofa could go in front of the fireplace with a couple of chairs on either side. A carpet would hide the unpolished floors and she could make some flowered draperies to brighten up the narrow windows.

Julia looked over and saw that her husband was still waiting for an answer. "Of course I can make it livable," she told him. "How soon can you take me into Watertown to go shopping?"

Watertown was a few miles inland from Sackett's Harbor. Ulysses drove her in the following Saturday. "How much can we spend?" Julia asked as they approached the outskirts of the city.

Ulysses shrugged. "Just pick out what you like," he said. "Then we'll worry about the price."

"We can't do that," Julia announced. "It isn't business-like."

She reached into her bag and pulled out a yellow pencil and a black leather notebook. "I'm going to keep careful track of all the money you give me to run the house," she told him. "I don't want to spend a penny more than we can afford."

Ulysses was impressed. "I thought I married a social butterfly," he said. "You're hard-headed enough to take over my job as quartermaster."

Ulysses had become the regimental quartermaster when the fighting ended in Mexico. It was his job to keep track of the Fourth Infantry's supplies. He had to know how many men needed new uniforms, how many pairs of shoes were worn out and had to be replaced, how many cots and blankets were on hand and how many more should be ordered. His desk was always piled high with ledgers and requisition forms. "I don't know why they gave me this job," he confided to Julia. "I'm the worst person in the world for keeping records and files. If somebody hands me a slip of paper to mind, the only thing I can think of to do with it is put it in my pocket."

A few weeks after they arrived at Madison Barracks, the Grants had their first taste of winter in northern New York State. An icy wind blew in from Lake Ontario, sleet scratched against the windows of their drafty house and the snow piled up so high on the doorstep that a pair of army privates had to shovel them out in the morning.

"I should have resigned from the army and stayed in

sunny Mexico," Ulysses moaned one morning as he stomped downstairs to breakfast.

"And what would have become of me?" Julia demanded, ladling out his oatmeal.

"You'd be an old maid, I guess," he replied casually.

When Julia threatened to dump the pan of hot oatmeal into his lap, Ulysses kissed her quickly and assured her that he would rather be freezing with her in Sackett's Harbor than basking alone in the Mexican sunshine.

Julia, true to her promise, had transformed the cramped quarters into an attractive home. Ulysses was so proud of it that on the spur of the moment one evening, he invited two of his fellow officers home for dinner.

Julia gasped when the unexpected guests appeared on her doorstep and refused to let them in the house. "I'm not good enough to cook for company," she stammered apologetically. "Would you mind coming back another night?"

The officers obligingly retreated and said they would get their dinner in the mess hall. When they had left, Julia glared at her husband. "You should have told me you were inviting them," she said. "I need a little more practice before I start entertaining at dinner."

Ulysses was amused by her annoyance. "If you didn't feel qualified, I could have cooked for them," he said cheerfully. "I once roasted a turkey over the fireplace in my room at West Point."

Julia nodded knowingly. "Fred told me about that," she said, "and he told me that you almost got expelled for it, too."

A few nights later, Ulysses came home and found the table set with the hand-painted dishes Julia had received for a wedding present. A crystal water goblet stood at each place and a pair of silver candlesticks flanked the bowl of artificial flowers in the center. "What's this?" he asked in surprise. "A party?"

"No," Julia told him, "it's a dress rehearsal. If this dinner goes well you can bring your friends home tomorrow night."

Julia enjoyed the elaborate dinners her mother had served at White Haven but with no one to help her in the kitchen, she kept her own menu as simple as possible. Ulysses pronounced it the best meal he had ever eaten and when his friends returned the following evening, they were just as effusive in their praise. When they first arrived, however, they could not resist poking fun at Julia for her reluctance to admit them on their first visit.

One of the young officers peered cautiously around the front door. "Are you sure it's all right for us to come in?" he said.

"Do you want us to come back another day?" his friend teased.

"Oh, hush, both of you," Julia scolded cheerfully as she led them into the parlor. "Or I'll make you come out in the kitchen and help me wash the dishes."

Ulysses was convinced that his orders to Sackett's Harbor had been issued by mistake. He wrote to his commanding officer as soon as he arrived at Madison Barracks and found there had indeed been an error. Lieutenant Grant was supposed to have been assigned to the regimental headquarters in Detroit. By the time his new orders arrived, Lake Ontario was clogged with ice and the Great Lakes steamers had discontinued their service until spring.

Cold and unpleasant as it was, the winter at Sackett's Harbor passed with amazing speed. Ulysses and Julia became friendly with several other lieutenants and their wives and although Julia was often teased about not letting her first dinner guests into the house, she soon became one of the most popular hostesses on the post.

By March, the Great Lakes steamers were running again and the Grants began packing for the move to Detroit.

Julia was cleaning out one of her dresser drawers when she came across the quilt she had hoped to finish during her stay at Madison Barracks. She had not added a single square to it.

"When we get to Detroit," she vowed, stuffing it into one of her trunks, "the second thing I'm going to do is finish this quilt."

Her husband looked puzzled. "The second thing?" he said. "What's the first?"

Julia's brown eyes danced with amusement. "Write to my father," she said, "and tell him that I survived the winter in Sackett's Harbor without getting double pneumonia!"

VIII

DETROIT REMINDED JULIA of St. Louis. It had a busy waterfront and, like her native city, it was once a French settlement so French names and customs were still common.

The Grants hired a buggy to take them from the steamboat landing to the hotel where they had rented rooms until they found a permanent place to live. Julia could not help gaping at the rows of attractive shops they passed along the way. She stared at the elegant carriages and high-stepping horses and sighed every time she caught sight of a fashionably dressed lady.

The plain brown cloak she had worn so often in Sackett's Harbor suddenly struck her as old and ugly. "All the ladies look so stylish here," she whispered to Ulysses. "I feel like a country bumpkin."

He squeezed her hand reassuringly and said, "You'll look just as smart as they do once you get your trunk unpacked."

Julia had bought a number of attractive outfits for her trousseau. There had been little chance to wear them at Madison Barracks but things were going to be different here. Even Ulysses sensed it. He glanced down at his dark blue uniform and said, "I think I'll order myself a new frock coat. This one is beginning to look shabby."

The barracks in Detroit had only a limited number of officers' quarters. Most of the married men rented houses nearby. Ulysses and Julia found a small cottage on the east side of town. The neighborhood was not particularly fashionable but Julia did not care. The house was comfortable and the rent was cheap. Some of the other houses on the block were rented by immigrants who had come to Detroit to work in the iron foundries, but one of their neighbors was an army captain named John Gore who was stationed at the barracks with Ulysses.

Julia liked John Gore at once. He was a tall sandy-haired man with a boyish smile and an irrepressible sense of humor. His wife Sarah was equally good-natured and she and Julia soon became close friends. It was Sarah who told the Grants about the weekly cotillions that were held at the Michigan Exchange Hotel. "They're great fun," she said. "You and Ulysses must come with us next Saturday night."

Julia looked dubious. "Ulysses isn't much of a dancer," she said, "but maybe I can persuade him."

She broached the subject at dinner that evening and Ulysses, in spite of his distaste for dancing, said it sounded like a good idea. For the next few months, the Grants and the Gores rarely missed a cotillion. Julia, whose feet started tapping the instant she heard music, danced with every officer in the ballroom. Ulysses took advantage of her popularity to escape into the hotel's taproom for a glass of whiskey and some army talk with his friends.

The winter after they moved to Detroit, Ulysses grew a beard and started smoking a pipe. Julia teased him about turning into an old man. "How about you?" he retorted. "You haven't asked me to take you to a cotillion in weeks and you've started walking up and down stairs instead of running the way you used to."

"That's true," Julia admitted. "But I have a good excuse. We're going to have a baby in May."

Ulysses stared at her blankly for a minute. Then his face broke into a contented grin. "That's the best news I've heard in a long time," he said happily.

Now that Julia had given up going to cotillions, she rummaged through the linen closet and dragged out the unfinished quilt she had brought with her from Sackett's Harbor.

"Look what I found," she said to Ulysses when he came home from the barracks that evening.

"Don't tell me you're finally going to finish that thing!" he exclaimed.

Julia nodded. "This is the perfect time," she said.

For the next few evenings, Julia sat with her sewing basket at her side but she would no sooner start working than she'd sigh and begin to complain about the tediousness of making a quilt.

"Why don't you stop?" Ulysses suggested.

"No," Julia said firmly, "I'm going to finish this quilt if it takes me all year."

A few nights later, however, Ulysses noticed that she had put the sewing basket aside and was reading a novel. "Have you given up so soon?" he demanded.

"Of course not," Julia replied. "I'll go back to it just as soon as I finish this chapter."

The entire novel was finished before Julia even thought about the quilt again. By then it was the middle of April and there was no point in worrying about it. "Even if I did finish it," she said, "I couldn't use it until next winter anyway."

The house in Detroit had a small back porch, just big enough to hold a pair of high-backed rocking chairs. The weather was so mild that spring that Ulysses and Julia sat out there almost every evening holding hands and chatting.

Sometimes they talked about Ulysses' work. He found his quartermaster's job dull and confining and he wished he was doing something that would keep him out in the open air. "Maybe I should have become a farmer," he sighed one evening. "I think I would have been better at it."

"It isn't too late," Julia reminded him. "You could resign from the army and buy some land."

Ulysses pondered the possibility for a few minutes but in the end he shook his head. "A soldier's salary is bad enough," he said. "I couldn't possibly ask you to live on a farmer's income."

Julia was sure she could manage if she had to but Ulysses still said no. "I'll put up with being a quartermaster for a little while longer," he decided. "Maybe the army will find a new job for me someday."

Most of Ulysses and Julia's conversations that spring were about the baby that was due in May. Julia was certain it would be a boy.

"I'm hoping for a girl," Ulysses said, "with tiny hands and a sweet smile just like her mother's."

They had decided that Julia would return to White Haven for her confinement. "I'll miss you," Ulysses said, "but I'll feel much better if your mother and Mary Robinson are there to help you."

When it was time for Julia to leave for St. Louis, Sarah Gore helped her pack. "I'll give Ulysses his dinner while you're gone," she promised.

"And I'll see that he doesn't go dancing every night," her husband added with a wink. "We all know how much Ulysses likes to dance."

Julia had not been home in almost two years. She had forgotten how pretty White Haven was in the spring. The warm sunshine danced across the meadows and bounced in the wide windows. It spilled across her coverlet and awakened her each morning. When she came downstairs, Mary Robinson would have her breakfast all prepared—fluffy scrambled eggs, squares of golden cornbread, strawberry preserves, and scalding dark brown coffee.

"You're spoiling me, Mary," Julia complained. "How am I ever going to get used to fixing my own breakfast again?"

"You'll manage," Mary told her with a smile.

Mrs. Dent had ordered the family bassinet taken down from the attic. The white wicker cradle had served as a bed for each of her sons and daughters and she was happy to see it being used for still another generation of the family.

Nellie and Emma volunteered to decorate the bassinet but they were in a quandary over what color ribbons to sew on the frilly dotted swiss skirt. Emma wanted pink because it was her favorite color. Nellie thought yellow would be better. "What do you say, Julia?" they finally asked their sister.

"Blue," she replied at once. "Blue is for boys."

"But suppose it's a girl?" Nellie said.

"If it's a girl she'll have Ulysses' blue eyes," Julia declared. "The ribbons will be a perfect match."

The baby was born on the thirtieth of May, and as Julia had hoped, it was a boy. She and Ulysses had picked out a name for him as they had sat rocking on their back porch in Detroit: Frederick Dent Grant.

Colonel Dent chortled with delight when he learned that his new grandson was going to bear his name. He had already pronounced little Fred the most beautiful baby in the world. Now he hovered over the infant's bassinet and studied him even more closely. "Yes, sir," he declared at last. "He's a bright little fella—sturdy, too. I wouldn't be a bit surprised if he grows up to be a general."

IX

Ulysses Grant saw his son for the first time when he arrived at White Haven a few weeks later to take Julia and the baby back to Detroit. Fred was sound asleep in his bassinet. Ulysses patted his small head and ran his finger across his soft pink cheek.

"Isn't he beautiful?" Julia whispered. "Father says he's going to be a general."

Her husband smiled. "As long as it's not a quartermaster," he said.

Julia could see that Ulysses had grown more dissatisfied than ever with his job. "Maybe you ought to get out of the army and take up farming," she suggested again. "There's plenty of good land right here in Missouri."

Julia, in fact, already owned sixty acres of Missouri soil that her father had given her for a wedding present. "That land hasn't even been cleared yet," Ulysses pointed out. "It would take a couple of years before I could turn it into a working farm."

He looked down at their small son sleeping contentedly in his cradle. "No," he said thoughtfully, "I think I'd better stick with the army."

Julia had been afraid she would be spoiled by all the pampering she received at White Haven. "I haven't made a bed or washed a dish in weeks," she told Ulysses. "I hope I haven't forgotten how."

Despite her fears, Julia had no trouble adjusting to housekeeping again. She hired an Irish girl to help with the laundry and heavy cleaning but she did everything else herself. She liked to cook and keep the house in order. But taking care of the baby was the most fun of all.

Fred was a plump, good-natured infant. Julia sometimes complained that she wasted half her day playing with him. Ulysses was even more infatuated with his son. As soon as he came home from the barracks at night, he would dash upstairs to the nursery to chuck him under the chin and listen to his happy gurgles.

With a baby to keep them home in the evenings, the Grants gave up attending the weekly cotillions at the Exchange Hotel. Instead, Julia and Sarah Gore took turns entertaining the other young officers and their wives at Saturday night suppers. After the table was cleared, they played cards or dominoes.

One night the Grants and the Gores gave a masquerade. They hired a fiddler and served a punch that Ulysses and John Gore spent half the afternoon concocting. Sarah and Julia each took a sip and pronounced it delicious. "What do you say, Grant," John said, clapping Ulysses on the back, "maybe we ought to resign from the army and open a tavern."

The masquerade was a great success. Julia was dressed as a fairy princess. Ulysses, reluctant to wear a costume at first, finally put on a pair of faded overalls and an old straw hat, stuck a corncob pipe in his mouth and called himself "Farmer" Grant.

Soon after Julia returned from St. Louis, a rumor began circulating that the Detroit barracks would soon be closed down and the regimental headquarters transferred to Madison Barracks.

Ulysses groaned when he heard the news. "Good old Madison Barracks," he said wryly, "a hundred miles from nowhere."

"If we go soon," Julia reminded him, "at least it will be warm."

"I refuse to believe that it's ever warm in Sackett's Harbor," her husband declared.

Julia laughed. "You mean I'll have to get to work on my quilt again. I hope I can remember where I put it."

The Detroit barracks did not close down immediately, however. It took another year for the official orders to come through. By then, it was summer again and Julia actually found herself looking forward to moving to Sackett's Harbor. Detroit was unbearably hot. Moreover, John and Sarah Gore were also being transferred, so the couples would not have to give up their Saturday night supper parties.

Sackett's Harbor looked far better in summer than it had in winter. The air smelled clean and fresh after the smoky chimneys of Detroit and Lake Ontario, no longer clogged with ice, was a sheet of sparkling blue.

Fred had celebrated his first birthday a month before they left Detroit. He was now toddling and starting to get into mischief. When the weather was warm, Julia entertained him with a walk down to the dock to watch the steamboats on the lake. It stayed light late on summer evenings and Ulysses got into the habit of taking him for another stroll before bedtime.

"I wonder how he'll stand staying in the house when winter comes," Julia said one evening as she and Ulysses were sitting on the porch holding hands and gazing at the stars in the August sky. "It's such a beautiful night," Ulysses replied. "Let's not spoil it by worrying about winter."

But summer soon slipped by. Fall went even faster and before long the first winds of winter were rattling through the Grants' flimsy frame house. One morning, Julia awoke to find the windows covered with frost and the pitcher of water on their washstand frozen solid.

"Winter has finally come," she announced with her teeth chattering.

As Julia had foreseen, Fred was not very happy about spending so much time in the house. But he managed to keep himself amused by emptying out the kitchen cupboards and banging on her pots and pans. Ulysses returned to their quarters each evening to find Julia holding her hands over her ears from the noise.

"And pretty soon it's going to be even more hectic," she exclaimed. "We're expecting another baby in July."

Ulysses welcomed the idea of a new baby in the family. He only wished it was not due in July. The regiment was scheduled to be transferred again that summer and he was afraid that Julia's pregnancy would keep her from accompanying him. He decided not to mention the possibility to Julia but she soon found out on her own.

Julia saw Sarah Gore at post dances and when the two couples visited back and forth in the evenings. But as the blustery March winds subsided and winter at last drew to a close, they were both out of the house more often. She met Sarah almost every day at the post office and occasionally Julia asked her old friend to join her when she took Fred for a walk around the post.

John Gore, an aide to the company commander, knew everything that was going on in the regiment. He passed much of the news along to Sarah and she in turn told

Julia. According to Sarah the latest rumor was that the Fourth Infantry would soon be leaving Sackett's Harbor and would be assigned to another post somewhere out west.

Julia's heart sank. She would have to remain behind until after the baby was born. It might be months before she and Ulysses saw each other again.

The two wives walked home together with Fred tagging along at their heels. Julia had said nothing to Sarah about her pregnancy so Sarah assumed that they would both be following their husbands out west. "I hope they send us to California," she said gaily. "I'd like to get my hands on some of that gold they've discovered out there."

Julia nodded and agreed that it would be an exciting trip. Secretly she was hoping that John Gore's information about the transfer would prove to be incorrect.

Neither Julia nor Ulysses mentioned the long separation that they both knew lay ahead of them but Julia noticed that her husband spent fewer evenings playing chess with his friends at the officers' club. Julia, in turn, got into the habit of bundling Fred into his crib a little bit earlier at night so she and Ulysses could have some extra time to sit and talk by themselves.

In late spring, the orders that Ulysses and Julia had been dreading finally came through. The Fourth Infantry was leaving Madison Barracks in June. They would sail from New York to Panama and from there march across the Isthmus and board another boat that would take them up the Pacific coast to Fort Vancouver, Oregon. The journey would take at least two months.

Several of the other wives, including Sarah Gore, were going with their husbands, but Ulysses refused to let Julia even consider the trip. "It means two long voyages," he said, "and a march across the Isthmus of Panama. I'd never forgive myself if anything happened to you."

They talked it over and decided that Julia ought to stay with Hannah and Jesse Grant in Bethel until after the new baby was born. "It will give them a chance to see Fred," he said, "and Fred will have a chance to see Ohio."

A few weeks later, Julia started packing. Their furniture and china would have to be stored until they set up housekeeping again—"Whenever that will be," Ulysses said glumly.

He was hoping that eventually Julia would join him in Oregon but he had no idea when they could manage this. Since she was not sailing on the army transports, he would have to find enough money to pay her passage on another ship.

The regiment left for New York in the middle of June. Julia tried to be brave as she kissed her husband good-bye and boarded the train for Ohio but there were tears in her eyes as she started out for Bethel. Fortunately, Fred was there to distract her. It took most of her energy to keep the lively two-year-old from squirming out of his seat and disturbing everyone else in the railroad car.

Jesse Grant met them at the station in Bethel. He and his wife were almost exactly as Julia remembered them from her wedding trip. Jesse could not stop crowing over his grandson while taciturn Hannah merely patted him on the head and observed dryly that he looked like a good boy.

Jesse Grant's leather business was thriving and he was also becoming a power in local politics but even though the Grants were financially better off than the Dents by now, their style of living remained drab and unpretentious.

Julia felt cooped up in their dark airless house with its heavy draperies and massive oak furniture. She could not help comparing it to White Haven. At this time of year, her mother would have vases of fresh flowers in all the rooms and the warm summer breezes would be wafting in from the veranda. It was odd that she and Ulysses got along so well and yet their families were completely different.

Julia tried to keep busy in Bethel. She sewed nightgowns and knitted booties for the new baby but, more often than not, her thoughts were with Ulysses on board the steamer bound for Panama. She had not heard from him since they sailed from New York and although she had written to him several times, she had no idea when he would receive her letters.

She found herself wishing that the baby would be born earlier than she expected. "The sooner it comes," she wrote to Ulysses, "the sooner I can join you at Fort Vancouver."

The baby was not early. It arrived right on schedule, on the 22nd of July. Hannah Grant assisted at the delivery. When she informed her daughter-in-law that she had another son, Julia was happier than she had been since Ulysses left for Panama. She took the newborn infant into her arms and hugged him close. "You're a little angel," she whispered. "I only wish your father could be here to share my joy."

X

THE BABY was christened Ulysses after his father but Jesse Grant insisted on calling him Buck because he had been born in the Buckeye State. The nickname stuck.

"Buck is a beautiful baby," Julia wrote to her husband. "I wish you could see him." She traced the infant's hand on a piece of paper and enclosed it in the envelope with her letter.

As soon as she was feeling well enough to travel, Julia returned to White Haven. She admired stern silent Hannah Grant but she did not find her very good company. Moreover, she had a strong suspicion that Jesse and Hannah did not approve of the attention she lavished on Fred and Buck. Their own children had been brought up with very few demonstrations of affection. Ulysses once told her that his mother hadn't even kissed him good-bye when he left for West Point.

Julia knew she would feel more relaxed in her own parents' house. Laughter and good conversation abounded there and Colonel and Mrs. Dent believed that babies were born to be fussed over.

The Dents were happy to have their oldest daughter back home. Except for Emma, the rest of the family was scattered by now. Nellie was married and living in St. Louis. George and his wife lived there, too, but they were the only ones near home. Louis was in California, John had a job down south, and Fred was still in the army.

Mrs. Dent took little Buck in her arms and started clucking over him right away. Colonel Dent swooped Fred off the floor in an enthusiastic hug. "Things have been too quiet around here," he chuckled. "We need a pair of mischief-makers to liven things up."

Ulysses had been gone for two months and Julia had yet to receive a letter from him. She had reason to be worried. The newspapers had been following the Fourth Infantry's progress across the Isthmus of Panama and every day the headlines proclaimed: DISASTER! MORE DIE IN TROPICS!

The regiment had been hit by an epidemic of cholera. Seven hundred soldiers and another hundred wives and children had left New York. According to the reports in the newspapers, over two hundred of them were dead.

Julia was beside herself with anxiety. Finally at the end of August, Ulysses' first letter arrived. He was in good health, he told her, and grateful that the troops had left sweltering Panama and were at last on board the ships that would take them up the Pacific to Oregon. He spared her most of the details of the wretched journey but he did tell her that one of the officers who had died of cholera was their friend John Gore.

Julia heard more about the nightmarish march a few weeks later when Sarah Gore stopped at White Haven for a brief visit before returning to her parents' home in Kentucky.

The Fourth Infantry had arrived in Panama in the middle of the rainy season. The pack mules that carried their baggage could hardly struggle through the mud.

"We could have survived the rains and the muck,"

Sarah said, "but then the cholera started. It struck without warning. One minute a man would be perfectly healthy. The next minute he'd be doubled up with cramps."

Sarah told Julia how John had been playing euchre with Ulysses and another officer one evening when he suddenly dropped his cards and gasped, "I've got the cholera!"

"Ulysses didn't want to alarm him," Sarah said, "so he told him that perhaps he had only eaten something that disagreed with him." She shook her head sadly. "He was dead before morning."

When Julia marveled at how well Sarah was bearing her grief, the young widow smiled wanly. "I cried so much on the boat back from Panama," she said, "I don't think there are any more tears left to shed."

Once the Fourth Infantry reached Fort Vancouver, Ulysses' letters were more frequent. He had little to say about his new post. Most of the time he talked about Julia and the children and how much he missed them all. He still hoped to send for them and was trying to earn enough money to pay their passage.

None of his money-making ventures were successful. He and another officer leased a farm and started cultivating potatoes but the Columbia River overflowed and destroyed the entire crop. Next they bought some chickens and chartered a boat to ship them to market in San Francisco. Unfortunately, the chickens died on the voyage and the men lost all the money they had put into the deal.

Although Ulysses tried to joke about his bad luck, his losses were a bitter blow. Nothing else was going well either. He disliked his quartermaster's job more than ever; he missed Julia and their two sons.

In October, Ulysses was promoted to captain and transferred to Fort Humboldt in California. At first he was cheered by the increase in pay that went with his new rank but the prices in California were so high that he soon realized it would not be enough to support his family even if he could manage to pay their way out.

At White Haven, Julia was also lonely, but she at least had her family and children to keep her company. Ulysses had only other army men. Their principal diversion at the end of the day was drinking whiskey and Ulysses got into the habit of joining them. A few drinks helped him forget how much he missed his pretty young wife.

By the spring of 1854, Captain Grant had been away from home for almost two years. He was sick of being a quartermaster and tired of being a soldier. He wanted to go home and see Julia and Fred and get acquainted with the young son he had never met.

To make matters worse, the commander at Fort Humboldt was a colonel Ulysses had known and disliked at Jefferson Barracks. The officer had even less use for Grant and seized on every excuse to find fault with him. One day Ulysses abruptly decided that he had had his fill of army life. He wrote a terse letter to the Adjutant General in Washington resigning his commission and asking to be relieved of his command. The resignation was accepted without comment and the ex-officer left Fort Humboldt at the beginning of May. Taking time only to write a brief letter telling Julia what he had done, Ulysses boarded the first boat he could find to New York.

He would have preferred to go straight to St. Louis but one of the merchants he had ordered supplies from at Madison Barracks owed him some money. The man's wife had been ill and business was bad and he had gotten into the habit of borrowing five or ten dollars from the company quartermaster each week. By the time Ulysses left Sackett's Harbor, the merchant owed him over a thousand dollars. Ulysses hoped to collect the money before returning to White Haven but he arrived in Sackett's Harbor to discover that the man had finally gone bankrupt and there was no hope of recovering the debt.

Disappointed and practically penniless, Ulysses returned to New York and looked up Simon Buckner, an old friend from West Point who had served with him in Mexico. Buckner remembered Sam Grant well. He treated him to dinner, offered him a room for the night and advanced him enough money to pay his way back to St. Louis.

Ulysses arrived at White Haven one summer afternoon about two weeks later. Two small boys were playing on the front lawn. He knew at once they must be his sons. Before he could introduce himself to the boys, the front door flew open and Julia came racing across the lawn and hurled herself into his arms. "Oh, Ulysses," she sighed, "I'm *so* glad you're home."

Fred and Buck sized up the bearded stranger who seemed so happy to meet them and decided that they approved of him. Ten minutes later, they were holding his hands and telling him all about the new kittens that had just been born in the barn.

Mrs. Dent embraced her son-in-law warmly. He looked worried and tired, she thought, older than his thirty-one years. Colonel Dent was less cordial. He thought Ulysses had been a fool to resign from the army so abruptly and he could not resist saying so at the dinner table.

Jesse Grant, who had always taken great pride in his soldier son, was even more outraged. He had written to

the Secretary of War, Jefferson Davis, and asked him to reconsider the resignation and give the homesick captain a leave of absence instead. Davis had refused.

"And now," Ulysses told Julia wearily, "I have to go home and ask my father to help me find a job."

Julia patted his hand sympathetically. "I'll go with you," she said. "We'll face him together."

It was not a pleasant visit for either of them. Hannah Grant said nothing about her son's return to civilian life but Jesse was still fuming. At first, he refused to give Ulysses any help in finding a job. Then he relented and said that he might be able to find a place for him in the leather goods store he owned in Galena, Illinois. But only on one condition: Julia and the children could not join him there. They would have to stay behind and live with her family in St. Louis.

"Absolutely not," Ulysses told his father curtly.

Julia was equally irate at the condition Jesse Grant laid down. "After two years away from you," she told her husband, "I don't ever want to let you out of my sight."

Disheartened, the Grants boarded the steamboat for St. Louis the next day. Julia usually tried to take a positive approach when things were going badly but the only bright spot she could discover was that at least the journey would give them a few days without either of their fathers glaring at Ulysses and making pointed remarks about his rashness.

Ulysses' predicament was the only thing they talked about all the way down the Ohio River and back up the Mississippi to St. Louis. By the time the boat landed they had reached a decision.

Ulysses would have to start farming the sixty acres of

land that Julia's father had given her as a wedding present.

It was not going to be an easy job. Trees had to be chopped down, livestock purchased, and men hired to help plow and plant the crops. However, Jesse Grant grudgingly offered his son a thousand dollars to get started in his new career and Colonel Dent said that Julia and Ulysses were welcome to stay at White Haven until they could afford to build a house of their own.

They would have preferred to be by themselves but there was no other choice. "I just hope you can get along with Father," Julia told her husband. "He seems to disapprove of you more now than he did when we were courting."

"Your father can be very difficult," Ulysses said, "but then so can mine. I'm afraid we'll just have to put up with both of them."

They sat for a minute staring glumly at the floor. Then Julia reached over and took her husband's hand. "We'll be all right," she said, "I know we will."

Ulysses nodded. "At least we're together again," he said. "That's the most important thing."

XI

THE COMPROMISE OF 1850 put an end to the arguments over slavery for a while. It kept the Northerners happy by admitting California to the Union as a free state and it kept the Southerners happy by including a stricter law against fugitive slaves.

Colonel Dent calmed down and stopped fuming about the "Yankee abolitionists" but now more than ever his wrath was directed at his jobless son-in-law.

Ulysses had started clearing a small patch of forest so he could begin farming Julia's land. He worked alone, hacking away at the thick underbrush and chopping down trees that had been standing for centuries. He squared off some of the logs and put them aside for the house he planned to build for his family, but most of the wood was chopped up and stacked neatly in cords. Every house in the neighborhood had at least two or three fireplaces and there was money to be made selling cord wood to burn in them.

The money was hardly enough to support a wife and two children so the Grants were still dependent on Colonel Dent's hospitality at White Haven. Ulysses was hoping it would not be for long.

Whenever Colonel Dent scoffed at his son-in-law's "wood-peddling," Ellen Dent was quick to defend him.

"Ulysses is having a hard time now," she would say, "but things will work out all right. I know they will."

Mrs. Dent saw how Ulysses winced every time her husband glared at his work clothes or poked fun at the old horse and wagon he used to haul his wood. Without saying anything to the rest of the family, she wrote a letter to her son Louis who had moved to California.

Before he left, Louis had built himself a small cottage about three miles down the road from White Haven. He called it Wish-ton-Wish, the Indian word for whippoorwill. The house had been empty for several years now. Mrs. Dent wondered if Julia and Ulysses might borrow it. "Give them the key," Louis wrote back, "and tell them to make themselves at home."

Julia showed the letter to Ulysses. "It isn't our own house yet," she said, "but it's a step in the right direction."

"Any place that's three miles away from your father is a step in the right direction," he replied sourly. "How soon can we move?"

They rode over to Wish-ton-Wish with Fred and Buck the next day. One of Colonel Dent's slaves followed them in a wagon with their clothing and some provisions from Mary Robinson's kitchen and they were settled in the cottage by evening.

The boys were almost as happy about the move as their parents. Wish-ton-Wish was set deep in a grove of oak trees. It was a fine place to play hide-and-seek or stalking Indians and at night they could listen to the call of the whippoorwills as they dropped off to sleep.

Ulysses' firewood business earned him only a few dollars a week but he and Julia managed to scrape by on it. They raised their own vegetables and kept a few chickens. Ulysses removed the insignias from his old army uniforms and wore them for work clothes and Julia cut up the worn-out dresses from her trousseau to make trousers for Fred and Buck.

The summer of 1855 was a memorable one. On the fourth of July, Julia gave birth to the Grants' third child and only daughter. They christened her Ellen after her grandmother but she was never called anything but Nellie.

Fred and Buck were too excited by the fourth of July fireworks to pay much attention to their new baby sister. They were impressed, though, when their father suggested that the parades and celebrations were all being held in Nellie's honor. "It looks like everybody in the country is glad she's here," he told them with a twinkle in his eye.

That same summer, Ulysses began digging the foundation for the house he had talked about building. Julia sketched out the floor plan—a sitting room and dining room on the first floor and three small bedrooms upstairs. Ulysses did most of the work himself, rising earlier in the morning so he would still have enough time to deliver his loads of wood and tend to the chores at Wish-ton-Wish.

The work went slowly. The wooden frame had to be erected, shingles cut for the roof and stones collected for the fireplaces and chimneys. Sometimes Julia walked over with Fred and Buck to watch its progress. She was impressed at the steady determined way Ulysses worked. When she mentioned it, he told her, "I promised myself a long time ago that once I make up my mind to do something, I'll never quit until it's done."

It was over a year before the cabin had reached the stage where Ulysses could invite their neighbors in for a house-raising. People came by the dozens, in buggies, on horseback, and on foot. The men pitched in to hoist the logs into place and to nail on the shingles that Ulysses had cut for the roof. The women brought hams and turkeys to feed the famished workers and the children scampered in and out playing tag and watching the log house taking shape before their eyes. The chinks between the logs had to be filled in with plaster and the windows and doors set in place. But in another two weeks the Grants had moved out of Wish-ton-Wish and were finally settled in their own home.

Ulysses named the farm Hardscrabble. "It doesn't sound as fancy as White Haven," he said, with an apologetic smile, "but it doesn't look as fancy either."

Julia couldn't argue. Hardscrabble's sixty acres were nothing compared to White Haven's thousand and the log cabin they lived in was not much larger than the houses Colonel Dent provided for his slaves.

"Don't you ever wish you'd married a rich man as your father wanted you to?" Ulysses asked his wife one evening.

"No," she responded firmly, "and besides, we aren't going to be poor forever."

Julia tended her new house as cheerfully and lovingly as if it were a splendid mansion. Her hand-painted china was carefully arranged on the shelves in the dining room cupboard; she made curtains for all the windows and laid out a garden by the front steps.

For the first few months, the Grants were happy at Hardscrabble. In the evening while Julia washed the dinner dishes and little Nellie slumbered in her cradle, Fred and Buck would sit in front of the fireplace in the sitting room and listen to their father tell stories about his army days.

Occasionally Ulysses ran into some of his soldier friends

in St. Louis. Sometimes they stared at his farmer's clothes and down-at-the-heel boots. More often, they clapped him on the back and invited him to join them at the Planter's Hotel for a meal or a game of cards.

Julia rarely went into town anymore. There was no money for ball gowns or opera tickets and even if there had been, she and Ulysses did not own a buggy for traveling. Besides, she was expecting another baby.

The baby was due in February, 1858, and during the long weeks before his birth, the Grants endured some difficult times at Hardscrabble. Ulysses continued to sell wood but he had also cleared enough land to start raising a few crops. The income they brought him scarcely covered the cost of his tools and supplies. At Christmas he was so short of money that he had to pawn his gold watch to buy presents for Julia and the children.

On top of their financial problems, Julia's mother was taken sick in December and died a few weeks later. Ulysses was as stricken as Julia at Ellen Dent's death. "She always believed in me and stood up for me," he said sorrowfully. "I'm going to miss her."

On February 6, Julia gave birth to her fourth child. It was another boy and they named him Jesse Root Grant after his grandfather in Ohio. Ulysses held the new baby in his arms and Julia saw him laugh for the first time in weeks.

By spring the little farm had grown into a more profitable enterprise but then the Grant household was struck by illness. First Fred developed typhoid fever and almost died. Then Ulysses came down with a raging fever and fits of trembling. The doctor diagnosed the illness as ague, an ailment that had plagued Ulysses as a boy and had also struck him during his final semester at West Point. "I've licked it before and I'm sure I can do it again," he told Julia weakly.

The fever eventually subsided but there seemed to be no cure for the trembling. Several times Ulysses was stricken in the fields and had to stop plowing in the middle of a furrow and stagger back to the cabin until he recovered.

Another time he had an attack when he was driving into town with a wagon-load of potatoes. Several of his neighbors saw his unsteady hands on the reins and the rumor soon started that Ulysses Grant was driving around drunk.

The doctor thought the ague might be caused by overwork. "Give up the farm," he advised, "and find an easier job in town."

Ulysses was in despair at the news. He liked farming and he was sure that in time he would be successful at it. Moreover he had no idea what kind of job he could find in St. Louis. His West Point education had prepared him to be a soldier and the only place for soldiers was in the army.

Ulysses hated to ask Colonel Dent for help but there was no one else to turn to. To his amazement, the Colonel was sympathetic and promised to see what he could do.

"My sister's boy Harry Boggs has a pretty good real estate business," he said. "Maybe he can find a place for you."

When Ulysses stopped in at Harry Boggs' office to discuss the possibility, Boggs was not particularly impressed with him. But he did think that his army background might be helpful. There was a tidy profit to be made renting houses to the officers who were stationed at Jefferson Barracks. "Some of them are old friends of yours," he told

Ulysses. "You can persuade them to do business with us."

The Grants leased Hardscrabble and rented a small house in a rundown section of St. Louis. It was not as comfortable as the log cabin and when Julia looked out the kitchen window, instead of grass and trees all she could see was a dirt yard and an ugly back fence. It was a far cry from the formal gardens at the O'Fallons' house on the other side of town.

Ulysses was hopeless as a real estate salesman. He refused to talk the young officers into paying more rent than they could afford and he did not have the heart to collect money from poor tenants. Whenever anyone gave him a hard-luck story and told him they could not pay the rent, he invariably lent them the money out of his own pocket.

Colonel Dent heard about his soft attitude and was furious. "At that rate," he snorted, "you'll soon be the poorest man in St. Louis."

The real estate partnership of Boggs & Grant collapsed after a few months. Harry Boggs wanted a more forceful man in his office and Ulysses wanted to work at something he knew more about. He talked to a number of people in St. Louis and soon discovered that the post of county engineer was vacant.

"It's the perfect job," he told Julia. "The salary is good and I'll be able to use the engineering I studied at West Point."

Ulysses was sure he had better qualifications than anyone else for the job, but just to be on the safe side he asked Colonel Dent to put in a good word for him with the county commissioners who made the appointment. There was one problem that he had not anticipated.

The issue of slavery, which appeared to be settled after

the Compromise of 1850, had heated up again after the Dred Scott decision in 1857. At that time the Supreme Court had declared that slaves had no rights as citizens. It also decreed that Congress could not prohibit slavery in newly acquired territories. The Southerners considered the decision a major victory for their cause but the opponents of slavery were outraged at it. The arguments were particularly bitter in Missouri, where slavery was permitted but where a large number of citizens were against it.

The majority of the commissioners who had to pass on Ulysses Grant's appointment as county engineer were against slavery. They knew nothing about Grant's views on the subject, but when they saw that he had been recommended by Frederick Dent, they immediately turned him down. They assumed that any relative of Frederick Dent's shared his southern sympathies.

Julia cried when she heard that her husband had not been hired, but Ulysses only clenched his teeth in anger and again set out on his quest for work. His luck appeared to be changing when he obtained a job as a clerk at the Customs House in St. Louis, but two months later the man who had appointed him died. His successor dismissed Ulysses and gave the job to one of his relatives.

The winter of 1859 was a time of decision for Julia and Ulysses. Ulysses could see no hope of earning a living in St. Louis and he was talking about going to Colorado or New Mexico where the prospects might be better. Colonel Dent sneered at the plan. "If you're a failure here," he said coldly, "you'll be a failure out there, too."

Ulysses was furious at his father-in-law, and even Julia found it hard to be civil to him. They were also growing tired of the constant wrangling over slavery that surrounded them in Missouri.

One evening, Ulysses sat down and wrote a letter to Jesse Grant. "It's time to give up on St. Louis," he told Julia in a quiet but determined voice. "If my father can find a job for me, I'm going to take it and get out of here."

Julia accepted his decision without a murmur of complaint. St. Louis had been her home for thirty-four years but she realized that the time had come to find a new home in the North.

XII

JESSE GRANT had finally stopped brooding about Ulysses' resignation from the army. He had too many other things on his mind. His sons Orvil and Simpson had taken over his tannery and leather business; but Simpson was in poor health and Orvil was too young to run things by himself. Jesse gave a sigh of relief when his oldest son's letter arrived, and wrote back quickly to invite him to join the firm.

Ulysses had worked in the tannery as a young man and hated it, but his new job would be different. Jesse wanted him to keep the accounts and balance the books in the store in Galena, Illinois. The salary he offered was more than Ulysses had earned since his army days.

"I'll start packing tomorrow," Julia said when Jesse Grant's letter arrived. "We can leave St. Louis by the end of the week."

A few days later, the Grants and their four children boarded the steamboat for Galena. Jesse was too young to have any opinion about the trip, but Fred, Buck and Nellie found it a great adventure. They wanted to spend the whole journey standing with their father on the upper deck.

Fred was fascinated by the houses and church steeples slipping by on the shore. Buck liked to watch the deckhands coiling the thick ropes that secured the ship to the dock, and Nellie could hardly take her eyes off the spinning paddle wheel and the foamy white water it spewed into the river.

"I want to be a riverboat captain when I grow up," Buck decided.

"I don't," Fred said stoutly. "I'm going to West Point to become a soldier."

The children were wide-eyed at their first sight of Galena. "It looks like it's built on shelves," Nellie announced gleefully.

Unlike St. Louis which lay on flat ground, the city stood on a series of bluffs that rose almost straight up on either side of the Mississippi. A narrow main street ran along the river and the houses were built on terraces above it.

The children were delighted to discover that their Uncle Simpson had found them a home on the topmost shelf. They could look down on Main Street from their parlor windows and watch the steamboats on the river beyond.

Six mornings a week, Ulysses marched down the long flight of wooden steps that led from his house on West Hill to the business district on Main Street. The J.R. Grant Leather Store sold saddles and harnesses, trunks and hatboxes, but Ulysses spent very little time in the front of the store. He worked at a desk in the back room and let the clerks take care of the customers.

In the evening Ulysses locked up the store, climbed back up the wooden steps and returned home. Three-year-old Jesse would be waiting for him at the front door with a fierce scowl on his baby face. His greeting was always the same. "Mister, do you want to fight?"

"I'm a man of peace," Ulysses would reply, "but I'll not be bullied by a person of your size."

At that Jesse would lunge at his father and the two of them would collapse in a heap on the floor. Ulysses pretended to struggle valiantly but in the end he always cried, "I give up," and let the triumphant toddler declare himself the winner of the wrestling match.

The Grants had left a mountain of unpaid bills behind them in St. Louis. They had also borrowed money from Julia's father to pay for their steamboat tickets and help them get settled in their new home. For the first few months in Galena, Ulysses sent back part of his salary to pay off his debts. "I'm afraid it doesn't leave you much to run the house on," he told Julia apologetically.

"I managed on less at Hardscrabble," she reminded him.

Julia kept careful track of her household accounts in a little black notebook just like the one she had first bought at Sackett's Harbor. She watched every penny. If the price of sugar went up, she stopped baking cakes. If the price of flannel went down, she bought several yards and made shirts and nightshirts for the men in the family and new nightgowns for herself and Nellie.

Occasionally Colonel Dent sent his daughter a few dollars with orders to buy herself a new hat or get something for the children. Julia knew he was trying to make up for the nasty things he had said to Ulysses and she accepted his unwritten apology.

The money was put to good use. Julia had always been fussy about clothes and now that she could afford it, she wanted her children to be well-dressed. Nellie who loved pretty things was no problem, but the boys complained because their mother made them wear shoes and stockings and shirtwaists that buttoned onto their trousers.

"Why can't we go barefoot and wear overalls and suspenders like everyone else?" Fred grumbled.

Buck agreed. "You make us dress like sissies," he pouted.

"Sissies!" Julia exclaimed, slapping them both on the backside. "No one who's seen you wrestling in the parlor or rampaging around the yard could ever mistake you for sissies!"

The Grants moved to Galena in April, 1860. Six months later, the nation was caught up in the excitement of a Presidential campaign. The opponents were two Illinois men: the United States Senator, Stephen A. Douglas, and a lanky, sad-faced lawyer from Springfield named Abraham Lincoln. The main issue was one that had been haunting the country for decades—slavery.

The South, the traditional stronghold of the Democrat party, refused to support the Democratic candidate Stephen Douglas. In the debates over the territories acquired after the Mexican War, Douglas had adopted a policy called popular sovereignty. He believed that the people in the individual territories should be allowed to make up their own minds whether or not to allow slavery within their borders. The Southerners objected to Douglas' stand on the grounds that slaves were a man's personal property and no territorial government had the right to outlaw them. They supported instead John Cabell Breckinridge as candidate of the Southern faction of the Democratic Party.

Without the support of the southern wing of his party, Stephen Douglas had no hope of winning the election. That meant that the next President of the United States would most certainly be Abraham Lincoln. Douglas was disliked south of the Mason-Dixon line, but Lincoln—who opposed the extension of slavery into the territories and regarded slaves as people, not property—was despised.

Everyone in Galena was talking about the forthcoming election. There were rallies and speeches almost every week and Fred and Buck hung out their bedroom windows at night watching the torchlight parades wending their way along Main Street like fiery snakes.

Ulysses and Julia were less worried about the election than they were about some of the rumors that began drifting into Galena from southern travelers who stopped at the DeSoto Hotel. If Abraham Lincoln was elected, the South planned to secede from the union and form their own confederacy of states. Ulysses heard the stories with an ominous frown. "If that happens," he told Julia, "we're going to have a civil war."

Abraham Lincoln was elected President in November, 1860. The governor of South Carolina promptly called a state convention and the delegates unanimously voted to secede from the union. Florida, Alabama, Georgia, Louisiana, and Texas soon followed.

By the time Abraham Lincoln left Illinois for his inauguration in Washington, most of the Southerners had resigned from Congress and Jefferson Davis had been elected president of the Confederate States of America. Everyone in the country wondered what was going to happen next.

Until then, Ulysses Grant had attracted very little attention in Galena, but after the election, word somehow got around that he was a former army man and had fought in the Mexican War. His neighbors began dropping into the leather goods store to ask him what he thought about the tense situation. Would it lead to war? Ulysses answered without hesitation. "Make no mistake about it," he said. "Both sides are ready to fight. They aren't bluffing."

In the end, it was the South that fired the first shot. In April a party of rebel soldiers attacked the Federal garrison at Fort Sumter in Charleston, South Carolina, and the Civil War had begun.

When the news reached Galena, Julia's first thought was that Ulysses was sure to be called back into the army. She decided not to worry about it just yet. Instead she got out the American flag and made Fred and Buck hang it from an upstairs window. "Now everyone knows we're on Mr. Lincoln's side," she said.

In the North the first order of business was raising an army. Richard Yates, the governor of Illinois, sent out a call for volunteers and the citizens of Galena voted to organize a company of their own. As the only man in town with military experience, Ulysses Grant was put in charge of it. He began to spend less time at the store and more time ordering uniforms and equipment and teaching the new soldiers to march and carry rifles.

Julia knew that her husband did not expect to remain a civilian for long, but at that time it seemed as though he had been completely overlooked. Other men from Galena were being commissioned captains and majors. Ulysses, with a West Point diploma and more than ten years' service in the army, thought he deserved to be a colonel. "Don't worry," Julia said confidently. "They just haven't come to your name yet."

Weeks passed and there was still no sign of a commission. Ulysses wrote to the governor of Illinois and to the War Department in Washington. He tried to talk to General George McClellan whom he had known at West Point, but the General was too busy to see him.

"Suppose they never come to my name," he said glumly.

"Don't be silly," Julia scolded. "Of course they will."

Ironically, Ulysses had already been offered a chance to serve with the Confederates. Right after the attack on Fort Sumter, Colonel Dent had written Julia a frantic letter, begging her to return to St. Louis at once. He would see to it that Ulysses became a brigadier general in Robert E. Lee's Confederate Army. Ulysses tore up the letter in disgust. "I'll have nothing to do with rebels," he snapped.

In June, almost two months after the war had started, Governor Richard Yates finally made Ulysses Grant a colonel and put him in command of the 21st Regiment of Illinois Volunteers. Julia could see from the way his eyes lit up when he read the letter that he was looking forward to becoming a soldier once again. "I won't be gone long," he promised as he left for the regiment's training camp in Springfield. "This whole thing will be settled in a few months."

XIII

ULYSSES' HOPES for an early end to the war faded quickly. "The Rebels have mustered an impressive army," he wrote home to Julia. "It looks like they're going to give us a good fight."

More than a few of the Rebel soldiers were men Ulysses had known at West Point or served with in Mexico. One of their generals was Simon Buckner who had loaned him the money to get back to St. Louis after he resigned from the army in 1854. Another was James Longstreet, who had been best man at his wedding. "I hope I don't run into old Pete on the battlefield," Ulysses wrote to Julia. "We might start talking about old times and forget all about fighting."

When the 21st Regiment finished their training, Ulysses came home for a few days' leave with Fred perched on the saddle in front of him.

Several of the officers from Galena had brought their teen-aged sons to the camp at Springfield to serve as aides. Fred was only eleven but he had insisted on going, too.

"Your mother will worry," his father told him.

"No, I won't," Julia replied and the matter was settled.

Fred was annoyed that his army service was over so

soon. "Father says I can't stay with the regiment anymore," he complained when Julia met them at the front gate. "Tell him it's all right."

"I'll do no such thing," his mother replied. "You've been in the army too long already. It's time you stayed home for a while."

Home, Ulysses and Julia had agreed, would continue to be Galena. Ulysses' parents had urged their daughter-in-law to stay with them while her husband was away but Julia never felt at ease in Hannah Grant's house. "I'll be fine right here," she assured her husband. "Don't forget, I have three strong men to look after me."

Ulysses patted his three sons affectionately on the head and gave Nellie a hug and a kiss. "Be good while I'm gone," he ordered them all, "and don't forget to write to me."

The newly commissioned colonel had no trouble readjusting to army life. He was better at commanding men and teaching them to fight than he had been at doling out uniforms and ordering shoes and cots. Less than two months after he entered the army he was promoted to brigadier general and given command of all the troops in southern Illinois and southeastern Missouri.

Ulysses' new headquarters was at Cairo, Illinois, near the junction of the Mississippi and Ohio rivers. Julia and the children took the steamboat down from Galena to visit him and stayed for almost two weeks. Nellie was shy in the strange surroundings but the boys had a fine time. Buck and Jesse made friends with the mess sergeant and got special rations of bread and butter with brown sugar sprinkled on top. Fred, who took army life more seriously, persuaded one of the officers to teach him to load and fire a rifle.

"You'll break your arm with that gun," his father warned him. "It weighs almost as much as you do."

"I can handle it," Fred said confidently. "Next time we come, I'm going to learn to fire a cannon."

On the way back to Galena, Julia stopped off to visit her father in St. Louis. Colonel Dent was angry because Missouri had voted to remain in the Union: he was even angrier because both his son and his son-in-law were serving in the Union Army. "The Rebels are going to win this fight," he insisted to Julia. "Just you wait and see."

A few people in St. Louis shared Colonel Dent's sentiments but most of Julia's old friends had no qualms about talking to a Yankee general's wife. Caroline O'Fallon invited her over for tea and made a great fuss over her children, and Louisa Boggs, the wife of her husband's former partner in the real estate business, insisted that she come to dinner.

Although Julia had told Ulysses she would remain in Galena, she was rarely there. She spent a few weeks with her father at White Haven and then traveled on to Covington, Kentucky, where Jesse and Hannah Grant now lived. She was still in Covington when Ulysses fought his first battle.

The Union Army had outlined a basic strategy for beating the Rebels. The Confederacy, with few railroads, was almost completely dependent on water transportation. If the North could seize control of its principal rivers, southern trade would be destroyed and the Rebels would be forced to surrender.

The plan called for Ulysses and his men to secure the Cumberland and Tennessee rivers. To do this, he had to attack two strategic Rebel strongholds, Fort Henry and Fort Donelson. He captured Fort Henry in February,

1862, and prepared to march against Fort Donelson twenty miles to the west.

For awhile the battle for the Fort appeared to be a stalemate. Grant's troops attacked but were driven back. When Union gunboats bombarded the fort from the river, they too withdrew in the face of the Confederate barrage. But the Confederates were surrounded, and could not hope to hold out for long. After a few days their commanders sent a message to the Union Army agreeing to surrender but asking for the best possible terms.

Ulysses Grant's reply was swift and definite. "No terms except unconditional and immediate surrender can be accepted," he wrote back.

The Southerners capitulated at once and Ulysses Grant marched into Fort Donelson to find himself face to face with his old friend Simon Buckner.

The Confederate general was in no mood to reminisce about old times. He surrendered his sword with an angry glare and sullenly informed his Yankee captor that he was also handing over 15,000 Confederate troops. Fort Donelson was the first major victory for the North and it won Ulysses Grant a promotion from brigadier to major general. It also prompted people to start joking that his first two initials, U.S., stood for "Unconditional Surrender" Grant.

No one had any complaints about General Grant's abilities as a soldier but there were rumors circulating around the army that he had a tendency to drink too much. His friends denied the tales but his enemies persisted in passing them along.

Julia heard about the rumors but was determined to ignore them. She was glad, however, that one of their neighbors from Galena, John Rawlins, was serving as her husband's aide. Rawlins made it his business to see that the stories about Ulysses Grant's drinking were stopped. A strict temperance man himself, he would not let his commanding officer have so much as a sip of wine at dinner. "I'd rather give one of my friends a glass of poison than a glass of whiskey," he told Julia.

Julia suspected that John Rawlins disapproved of women around an army camp as much as he did of whiskey, but she did not let that stop her from visiting her husband whenever she had the chance. She brought the children when she could, but when it was inconvenient, she left them in Galena with her Irish housekeeper, Maggie.

While Ulysses was poring over his maps and battle reports, Julia found plenty to keep her busy. She visited the men who were sick and talked to them about their wives and families. Sometimes she took a camp chair and sat in front of her husband's tent sewing buttons on his uniform. Ulysses was inclined to be careless about his appearance, but his officers noticed that he looked much neater when Julia was on hand to take care of his clothes.

The Union Army had pushed its way down from southern Illinois through Kentucky and western Tennessee and was now trying to gain control of the Mississippi River. Admiral David Farragut had captured New Orleans in the spring of 1862, but the Confederates still controlled the equally strategic port of Vicksburg.

Ulysses Grant started his march toward Vicksburg the following fall. He advanced into northern Mississippi and began setting up a supply depot at Holly Springs. His own headquarters were in Oxford, a few miles to the north.

The General's scouts had assured him that there were

no Rebel forces in the area so he sent off a note to Julia begging her to visit him. She came as quickly as she could, but apologized for coming alone. "The children have colds," she explained. "I thought it would be better if they stayed at home."

Ulysses sent one of his officers to find a place for Julia to stay in Holly Springs. The house he selected was a handsome white-pillared mansion that belonged to a southern planter named Harvey Walters. When Julia arrived, Mrs. Walters was standing in the front hall with an unhappy expression on her face. Julia turned at once to the two officers in blue who accompanied her. "Just leave my bags at the foot of the stairs," she said. "I'm sure I'm in perfectly safe hands."

When the officers had left, she offered her hand to her hostess. "It's bad enough to have an uninvited guest," she said, "but one that arrives with an armed escort is even worse. Please accept my apologies for imposing on you like this."

Mrs. Walters' cold stare softened into a wan smile. "You're very kind," she replied. "It makes our humiliation a little easier to bear."

Julia was having dinner at her husband's headquarters in Oxford a few nights later when a party of Rebels staged a surprise raid on Holly Springs. They burned the warehouses where the Union troops had stored their food and supplies and shot the soldiers who tried to defend them.

Hearing that General Grant's wife was staying with the Walters, one group of soldiers tried to break into the mansion and seize her belongings. Harvey Walters stood in the wide entrance hall and ordered them out of his house. "This is a war against soldiers," he told the raiders sternly. "Not against soldiers' wives."

The men retreated meekly and when John Rawlins rode over the next day to collect Julia's clothes, he found them carefully folded and packed. Julia sent him back with a note of thanks and her husband promptly issued an order instructing his troops not to trespass on the Walters property and to treat Mr. and Mrs. Walters with special consideration and courtesy.

Ulysses had been hailed as a hero for his capture of Fort Donelson but soon after that the Confederates had taken him by surprise at Shiloh, Tennessee. Thousands of men were slaughtered in the battle and the northern newspapers blamed Ulysses Grant for their deaths. A few editors angrily demanded that he be relieved of his command but President Lincoln refused. "I can't spare this man," he said bluntly. "He fights."

Ulysses' reputation as a general was completely restored when he succeeded in capturing Vicksburg and making the Mississippi a northern, instead of a southern, shipping lane. He first attacked the city in May of 1863, but after three unsuccessful assaults on the Confederate lines, he decided to give up the attacks and take the city by siege. If the Yankees waited long enough, the Rebels would run out of food and ammunition and finally be forced to surrender.

Julia made several visits to her husband's headquarters during the long months of the siege. She decided against bringing the three younger children with her, but Fred refused to stay home. He ate in the soldiers' mess, slept on a cot in his father's tent, and when Julia decided to go on to St. Louis for a visit with her father, he pleaded with her to let him stay behind.

Julia was afraid that at thirteen he was still too young for army life but Ulysses soon quieted her fears. "He's a good boy and he knows how to look out for himself," he said. "I don't think you have anything to worry about."

Vicksburg fell on the fourth of July, 1863. Julia was in her room at the Planter's House in St. Louis when the news reached her. In minutes a shouting mob had assembled in the street in front of the hotel. "Ulysses Grant. Ulysses Grant," they chanted. As Julia listened, the voices became louder and the chant changed to, "Mrs. Grant. Mrs. Grant."

She opened the long French windows and stepped out onto the balcony of her hotel room. The crowd greeted her with a tumultuous roar. Julia stood there smiling and waving to them, thrilled to see that her quiet, determined husband was on his way to becoming a national hero.

XIV

COLONEL DENT was disgruntled at his Yankee son-in-law's fame. Julia couldn't resist teasing him about it. "Isn't it about time you admitted that I married the right man after all?" she said.

The Colonel coughed and sputtered and finally conceded that if Vicksburg had to fall, he was glad it had fallen to Ulysses.

The capture of Vicksburg meant that Julia would be able to visit her husband again. Ulysses promised to send one of his aides to meet her at the steamboat. Instead of John Rawlins, whom she expected, she stepped off the gangplank and came face to face with another even more familiar figure.

"Fred!" she exclaimed, as she kissed her brother warmly. "What on earth are you doing here?"

"I've just been assigned to your husband's staff," he told her. "After all those years out west, he thought I ought to be closer to home."

Fred had never met the Grant children. He shook hands with each of them in turn and then clapped his namesake affectionately on the shoulder. "We'll have to get better acquainted," he said. "Your father tells me you're going to become a West Pointer some one of these days."

Ulysses always provided horses so Fred and Buck could ride when they came to visit him in camp. This time he had a surprise for Jesse—a sturdy Shetland pony named Rebel. Jesse clapped his hands with delight at the gift and demanded a ride at once. Ulysses complied by boosting the determined four-year-old up in the saddle and ordering one of the soldiers to take him on a short tour of the parade ground.

During the long siege of Vicksburg, the city had been bombarded with shells and rockets and pounded by cannon balls. Only a few houses survived the assault. Some were completely destroyed. Others were pockmarked with shell holes, their lawns and gardens ripped up, and their owners forced to find shelter in a network of caves just outside of town.

Appalled at the destruction, Julia begged her husband to treat the conquered citizens with kindness. Ulysses needed no urging. He gladly gave passes to women who wanted to leave Vicksburg and move to other parts of the south. When one of his aides seized some furniture for his commander's headquarters, Ulysses ordered it returned to the family who owned it.

One of Ulysses' closest friends in the army was General William Tecumseh Sherman. "Cump," as his friends called him, had brought his wife Ellen to Vicksburg and she and Julia spent a great deal of time together.

The Shermans also had four children. The oldest, nine-year-old Willy, liked to play with Buck and Nellie. Every morning promptly at ten o'clock he would appear at the Grants' back door. "Are Buck and Nellie home?" he would ask Julia eagerly. "Can they come out and play?"

One morning Willy failed to appear. At first Julia was

amused. "I thought I could set my clock by that young man," she said. "Now he's disappointed me."

When there was no sign of Willy the following day, Julia began to worry that he might be sick.

She rapped on the Shermans' door that afternoon. Ellen answered and Julia could see that she had been crying. "Is something wrong?" she inquired solicitously.

"It's Willy," Ellen replied in a hollow voice. "He has typhoid fever."

Cump Sherman was leading a Union march across Tennessee and Ellen was all alone. Julia came over every day to sit with her and try to cheer her up. "He's such a strong little boy," she told Ellen. "I'm sure he'll pull through."

But Willy grew steadily worse and a week later, died. "Poor Ellen," Julia said. "It must be horrible to lose a child."

Ulysses agreed. "I feel sorry for Cump, too," he said. "He was always so proud of Willy."

Not long after that, Julia noticed that Fred was pale and listless. He lost his usual interest in food and started complaining about pains in his stomach. Julia dosed him with peppermint tea; when that did not help, she decided to take him back with her to St. Louis.

"I don't think it's anything serious," she told Ulysses, "but there's so much illness here in Vicksburg, I think he'll be better off somewhere else."

When they got to Missouri, Fred's pains were worse and he was beginning to run a fever. Harry and Louisa Boggs had invited Julia to stay with them and by the time she had Fred settled in their guest room, she could see that he was a very sick boy. The doctor diagnosed his illness as dysentery, but Julia, not wanting to worry Ulysses, wrote and told him it was only a bout of indigestion.

A few days later, however, Fred developed pneumonia and Julia knew that she could spare her husband no longer. She sent him a telegram that afternoon. COME AT ONCE, it said. FRED GRAVELY ILL.

The worried mother spent almost all her time at her son's bedside. Willy Sherman was constantly in her thoughts. Clutching the small Bible she had owned since she was a girl, she prayed, "Please, dear Lord, don't take Fred away from us."

Julia hardly took her eyes off her son's flushed face. Once or twice she thought his breathing seemed fainter but the doctor assured her that Fred was still holding his own. "If he continues to do that for another twenty-four hours," he said, "I think he'll be all right."

Julia sat up all that night. By morning, Fred's forehead seemed cooler to her touch and when he spoke to her, he sounded almost like his old self. "I'm hungry," he murmured weakly. "Can I have some cinnamon toast?"

When the doctor came by later in the morning he found Fred propped up in bed with a breakfast tray on the table beside him.

A few minutes later, Ulysses appeared in his son's bedroom. His anxious frown dissolved into a smile of relief when he saw Fred sitting up in bed. "I thought you were supposed to be dying," he exclaimed, "and here you are cheerfully munching on cinnamon toast."

Fred gave him a crooked smile. "Just give me a day or two, and I'll be back helping you run the army."

With Fred on the road to recovery, Ulysses and Julia were able to relax and enjoy the few days they had together. They went to the opera house one evening to see a new play that Caroline O'Fallon had recommended. The usher had scarcely shown them to their box than everyone in the theater turned to look at them. Someone started clapping and in another instant the entire theater was giving General Grant a standing ovation. Ulysses was embarrassed by the applause, but Julia nudged him and whispered, "Stand up and take a bow."

He rose to his feet and bowed obediently. "I hope this isn't going to happen every time we go to a play," he muttered to Julia under his breath.

The night before Ulysses had to return to duty, Colonel John O'Fallon gave a banquet in his honor. It was a stag party and the guests included every man of importance in St. Louis. Julia laughed when she heard that her father was planning to attend. "Do you really think you should?" she teased. "After all, it's for a Yankee general."

The Colonel's face flushed. "I guess it's time to let bygones be bygones," he mumbled grudgingly.

The War Department in Washington was still rejoicing over the capture of Vicksburg when the North was faced with a major setback in Tennessee. The Union Army was trapped at Chattanooga; its supply lines were cut off by the enemy and it was in danger of either starving to death or being forced to surrender. Ulysses Grant was promptly given command of all the Union forces in the West and ordered to proceed to Tennessee to relieve the beleaguered troops.

Cump Sherman, who was occupying Memphis, came east to help him and several regiments from New York and Pennsylvania joined them. Under Grant's leadership, the army managed to reopen the supply lines to Chattanooga and drive the Rebels across the Tennessee line into Georgia. Ulysses was rewarded with a gold medal and a commendation from Congress. He was also promoted to supreme commander of the Union Army.

Julia read about her husband's appointment in the newspaper and rushed to send him a telegram of congratulations. She was sorry she could not be with him when he went to Washington to receive his promotion in person. Fred, who was still with the troops, accompanied his father instead and stood at his side in the White House when Abraham Lincoln formally gave Ulysses command of the Union forces.

Ulysses was so anxious to get back to his headquarters in Nashville that he declined Mrs. Lincoln's invitation to be the guest of honor at one of her receptions.

"If you'll excuse me, Ma'am," he said, "I have too much work to do."

Ulysses expected to be busy for the next few months mapping out plans to end the war. He planned to be spending a good deal of time in Washington conferring with the President and the Secretary of War and he suggested that Julia bring the children to the capital so he would be able to see them when he came.

On the way to Washington, Julia stopped in Philadelphia to buy some new clothes for herself and the children. Jesse, who hated to shop, was annoyed.

"We don't need new clothes!" he declared sullenly.

"Of course you do," Julia told him firmly. "You don't want everyone in Washington saying that General Grant's children look like ragamuffins."

Julia was glad she had bought a new outfit for herself, because she was no sooner settled at the Willard Hotel than she received an invitation to a White House reception.

She placed the stiff white card on the mantel and stared

at it for a long time. Then she did a small pirouette around the center of the room. "Imagine that," she said gaily, "I'm going to shake hands with the President of the United States."

A distinguished-looking colonel arrived to escort Julia to the reception. She doffed her cape at the White House door and gave a hasty pat to her hair before joining the line of people waiting to shake hands with the President. When it was her turn to be introduced, Abraham Lincoln's face broke into a warm smile. He took both her hands in his and said, "Welcome to Washington, Mrs. Grant—and thank you for lending the nation that brilliant husband of yours."

Julia returned to the hotel with tears of joy in her eyes. "I'll never forget this afternoon," she promised herself. "I'm as proud and happy as I was on my wedding day."

XV

ON HER FIRST VISIT TO the White House, Julia met Mary Lincoln and some of the other women who ruled Washington society. The wives of the senators and cabinet members were all eager to shake hands with the famous General Grant's wife. They crowded around her as she left, begging her to come to tea or to join them in their boxes at the theater.

When Ulysses arrived in town, he and Julia were swamped with more invitations. But for one of the few times in her life, Julia was reluctant to plunge into the social whirl. "It seems so frivolous," she said to Ulysses, "with a war going on." They attended a few parties, but without enthusiasm. "The only good thing I can say about them," Ulysses grumbled good-naturedly, "is that they make me happy to get back to camp."

By the spring of 1864, the Federal armies were preparing for an all-out advance against the Confederate capital at Richmond, Virginia. "Do you think they'll capture it?" Julia was asked at a reception one evening.

"Of course," she replied quietly. "Mr. Grant is a very obstinate man."

The attack on Richmond was going to be a long hard fight. To prepare for it, the Union Army set up an enormous supply depot on the James River at City Point, Virginia, about thirty miles from the Rebel capital.

"Things are going to be quiet around here for awhile," Ulysses wrote to Julia. "Bring the children down for a visit."

Julia was astonished to find City Point such a busy place. Transports and barges were lined up along the waterfront, unloading everything an army could possibly need—food and medicine, guns and ammunition, extra overcoats and boots.

"I never heard of City Point until I got your letter," Julia exclaimed when she arrived at her husband's new headquarters. "But look at the place. It's as busy as St. Louis."

Ulysses' quarters were a regulation army tent, but he thought Julia and the children would be more comfortable on board a small steamer anchored at one of the wharves. "Perfect," Julia exclaimed when she saw it. "The boys can fish from the stern and Nellie and I can sit on deck with our parasols and pretend that we're on our way to Paris."

Whenever he could spare the time from his official duties, Ulysses rushed over to the steamer to be with his wife and family. Sometimes he wrestled with Buck and Jesse on the floor of the boat's grand saloon; sometimes he read stories to Nellie. In the evening, when the youngsters were asleep in their bunks, he and Julia sat out on the deck gazing up at the summer sky. The war was uppermost in both their thoughts but they rarely mentioned it. Instead they talked about the children.

Julia was worried about all the school they had missed, traveling about the country to be with their father. She was particularly concerned about Fred, who had been with the army for months.

Ulysses agreed that it was time for his oldest son to get

back to his lessons. "Why don't you rent a house someplace here in the East?" he suggested. "The children could go to decent schools and you'd still be close enough to visit me whenever I sent for you."

The place they decided on was Burlington, New Jersey, just across the Delaware River from Philadelphia. Julia rented a rambling two-story house with a big front porch and a stable in the backyard for Jesse's beloved pony, Rebel.

Jesse, Buck, and Nellie thought the house was lovely, but Fred was not so enthusiastic. "I'd rather sleep in a tent in the field," he grumbled.

Julia laughed. "Try to put up with living in a house for a while," she said. "It won't hurt you."

Nellie was enrolled in Miss Kingdon's School for young ladies and when it turned out that the best boys' school in town was a military academy, Fred became resigned to his fate. "It may not be General Grant's army," he said with a sigh, "but I guess it will do until I get to West Point."

Julia was always on the lookout for a letter or telegram from Ulysses, but he surprised her one night by arriving in person. He stepped down from his private car when it pulled into the railroad station and walked over to the local constable who was standing on the platform. "They say I live here," he said quietly, "but I don't know where."

The constable held up a lantern and peered into the stranger's face. "Good heavens!" he exclaimed. "It's General Grant."

With great ceremony, the officer escorted the general to Wood Street and pointed out the house that Julia had rented. It was close to two in the morning but as soon as Ulysses rapped on the front door, an upstairs window flew open and Julia called down, "Is that you, Ulysses?" A moment later, she appeared at the door and let her husband into the house.

By morning, everyone in Burlington knew that Ulysses S. Grant was in town. He had just finished his breakfast and was settling back to enjoy a cigar with his coffee when there was a great commotion outside. Julia rushed to the door and found the front porch packed with people. The crowd spilled over onto the steps and stretched along the sidewalk.

Julia graciously invited them in, "But only a few at a time," she told them. Some of the visitors just stood and stared at the famous soldier. Others went up to him and shook his hand, murmuring a few words of thanks to him for saving the country. When they left the house, they lined up along the street and stood there hoping to catch another glimpse of their hero.

Ulysses was planning to catch a ten o'clock train to New York. "Put on your hat," he ordered Julia. "You're coming with me."

"On such short notice?" she gasped.

"Of course," he replied. "If you're married to a soldier, you have to learn to travel like one."

Julia spent the next two hours rushing around packing her valise and giving Maggie instructions for coping with the children. Miraculously, she was ready on time and she and Ulysses boarded the train to the cheers and waves of Ulysses' admirers who had followed them to the station.

The train took them as far as Jersey City. From there they had to take a ferry across the Hudson River to New York. When they arrived, the ferry landing was mobbed and a long line of policemen had to hold back the excited crowd.

Their reception was the same everywhere in New York.

Ulysses abandoned his uniform for civilian clothes, but still people recognized him. Whenever he sat down in a restaurant, the other diners turned to get a better look at him. When Julia went shopping at A.T. Stewart's, both customers and salesclerks came over and pressed her hand. "Tell your husband we all admire him," they would say. "We hope he gets this terrible war over with soon."

The trip to New York was a brief one. Two days later, Julia was back in Burlington and Ulysses was on his way to City Point. However, Julia took the children down for the Christmas holidays. Ulysses had given up his tent for the winter and was now living in a small house on a bluff overlooking the James River. Julia tied some evergreen branches with red ribbons and arranged them on the mantel in the tiny parlor. For Christmas dinner, she roasted a wild turkey that one of Ulysses' orderlies had shot in the woods.

The children had to return to school soon after the New Year. Julia took them home to New Jersey but once they were safe in Maggie's hands, she hurried back to Virginia to be with her husband again.

Ulysses' soldiers had been hammering away at Richmond's defenses all winter, but the Confederates showed no sign of surrendering. Julia could see how tense and anxious Ulysses was; for the next few months she became a steady commuter between Burlington and City Point.

Several times while she was there, President Lincoln arrived to confer with his commanding general. Occasionally, Mrs. Lincoln came with him. Julia soon discovered that the First Lady was not always as cordial as she had been when they first met at the White House. Mary Lincoln could be moody and irritable and she often flew into unexpected rages.

"Try to forgive her," Ulysses told Julia. "I suspect, from

things the President has said, that she is not a well woman."

Julia managed to handle Mrs. Lincoln with tact, but she never enjoyed her company and she was always happier when the President left his wife at home and brought their son Tad to City Point instead.

Julia had one tense moment during the twelve-month siege of Richmond. Word reached her husband's headquarters one night that a fleet of Confederate gunboats were heading down the James River towards City Point. Ulysses was sure it would never get past the Union defenses, but he left word before going to bed that if there was any further news, he was to be awakened at once.

It was after one when an orderly thumped on the Grants' bedroom door. "The Confederates have broken through," he reported. "They're heading downstream right now."

Ulysses leaped out of bed and threw on his clothes. By the time Julia got dressed he was already at his desk, writing out orders. Julia pulled up a chair beside him and said bluntly, "Are those gunboats going to shell this camp?"

"They will if they manage to get down here," her husband replied.

"What had I better do?" Julia said calmly.

Ulysses looked at her for a moment before replying. Then he said in an amused tone, "Well, the fact is, Julia, you oughtn't to be here."

One of Ulysses' aides suggested hiding Julia in the woods where she would be safe from the threatened attack, but Ulysses turned down the suggestion. "The gunboats aren't here yet," he said. "Let's wait a little while longer."

Still unruffled, Julia sat up with her husband till dawn, but the gunboats never appeared. In the morning they learned that the fleet had run aground a few miles above City Point and there was no further cause for alarm.

At the beginning of April, 1865, the Confederate forces in Richmond could hold out no longer and the victorious Union Army marched into the Rebel capital. A few days later, on April 9th, word reached City Point that General Lee had surrendered at the tiny village of Appomattox Court House.

Julia was with John Rawlins' wife, Emma, when she heard the news. The two women hugged each other excitedly. They had not seen their husbands for several weeks, but Julia was sure now they would be on their way home. "Let's have a party in honor of the victory," she suggested to Emma.

The two women prepared a roast chicken. Emma brought over a chocolate cake she had baked that morning and Julia placed a bowl of wildflowers in the center of the table. "Now," she said gaily, "all we need are our guests of honor."

Julia and Emma Rawlins sat up until midnight, waiting for their husbands. Emma finally fell asleep on the sofa and Julia tiptoed upstairs and stretched out on her bed. She awoke with a start when she heard the bedroom door open and found Ulysses standing by her side. She leaped up and smoothed her rumpled dress. "I didn't mean to fall asleep," she gasped.

Ulysses gave her a warm hug and a kiss, but when Julia asked him about the surrender at Appomattox, he refused to talk about it. The only thing he would tell her was that his boots had been muddy. "You would have been ashamed of me," he said ruefully, "but General Lee's offer took me by surprise and I had no time to change them."

Julia was stunned to discover that it was almost five in the morning. When she told Ulysses about the dinner party that she and Emma Rawlins had been planning, he laughed and suggested that they turn it into a breakfast instead.

They went downstairs and found Emma and John Rawlins waiting for them in the dining room. The chicken was cold by now but Julia served it anyway. A few minutes later, the four of them sat down at the table. Before they ate, Ulysses offered a prayer of thanksgiving that the war was over at last.

XVI

THE SURRENDER at Appomattox took place on a Sunday morning. The following Thursday, the Grants left City Point and went to Washington so Ulysses could talk to the Secretary of War about demobilizing his army and disposing of their equipment and supplies.

Everyone in the capital was celebrating the Union victory. Red, white, and blue bunting decorated the store fronts, posters of Abraham Lincoln and Ulysses Grant hung from the lampposts, and at night all the buildings in the city were ablaze with light.

"Isn't this exciting!" Julia exclaimed, standing at the window of their hotel room. "I only wish the children could be here to see it."

Julia had not seen her family for over a month and she was anxious to get back to Burlington as soon as possible. "If all goes well," Ulysses promised, "we should be able to leave tomorrow evening."

Julia was packing their bags the next morning when a message arrived from the White House. "Oh, dear," she exclaimed, ripping open the note and showing it to her husband. "The Lincolns want us to join them at Ford's theater tonight. What shall we do?"

Ulysses shrugged. "I don't mind," he said, "but I know you're not very fond of Mrs. Lincoln so I'll let you decide."

Julia had no trouble making up her mind. "I'll tell her we're sorry," she said, "but we have to get back to Burlington right away."

The Grants took an eight-o'clock train from Union Station. They had to change at Philadelphia and they stopped for a late supper at one of the downtown hotels. As soon as they entered the lobby they were met by a grim-faced messenger with a telegram for General Grant.

Ulysses' face grew grave as he read the message and Julia thought she saw tears welling in his eyes. "What is it?" she asked quickly.

Wordlessly, Ulysses handed her the yellow piece of paper and Julia stared in horror at the message: ABRAHAM LINCOLN SHOT AT FORD'S THEATER THIS EVENING. DOCTORS HOLD OUT LITTLE HOPE OF RECOVERY.

Ulysses and Julia were dumbfounded at the news. Ulysses had shaken hands with President Lincoln only a few hours before.

Julia wept softly and offered a prayer for the dying President and another prayer of gratitude that they had not accepted Mrs. Lincoln's invitation. "You might have been shot, too," she told her husband.

Ulysses pooh-poohed the idea but when the conspirators were apprehended a few weeks later, it was discovered that there had also been a plot to kill Ulysses Grant. Only his abrupt departure from Washington had foiled the would-be assassin.

The leader of the victorious Union forces remained the most popular man in the country. In the summer of 1865, he and Julia took the children on a trip through New York and New England. Every town they stopped in gave them a gala welcome. In Boston, Ulysses was awarded an honorary degree from Harvard College.

The most heartwarming episode of the Grants' journey occurred at the very end. When their train pulled into Galena, they were ushered into a waiting carriage and driven off for a reception at the DeSoto Hotel. Galena's Congressman Elihu Washburne welcomed them home and presented them with the deed to a fine brick house on Bouthillier Street. The townspeople had bought it as a token of esteem for their most illustrious citizen.

When the carriage deposited them on their new doorstep later that afternoon, Ulysses announced that all he wanted to do now was settle down and enjoy watching his children grow up. "That's a lovely idea," Julia agreed, "but I don't think the country will let you."

Congress had made Ulysses a full general. He became the first man to hold the rank since George Washington and the newspapers were saying that he was going to be the next President of the United States. Ulysses laughed whenever Julia mentioned it to him but she knew that a number of Republican politicians had asked him to consider the race and he had promised to think it over.

Whether Ulysses decided to go into politics or not, the Grants could not remain in Galena permanently. Ulysses was the supreme commander of the United States Army and his new headquarters were at the War Department in Washington.

Julia found a comfortable house on I Street for them to live in and when the carpets had been laid down and the draperies hung, she announced that it was time she joined the ranks of Washington's hostesses.

The Grants held their first reception on New Year's Day, 1866, with Julia wearing a rose silk gown that she had bought at A.T. Stewart's in New York.

That spring Fred received the appointment to the military academy that he had been dreaming about since his childhood. He departed for West Point in September, leaving only the three younger Grants for Julia to cope with. Buck was going to Harvard in another year and soon there would be only two.

The Grants had been in Washington for almost two years when the House of Representatives drew up impeachment charges against President Andrew Johnson. They accused him of violating the Tenure of Office Act by dismissing Edwin Staton as his Secretary of War.

Johnson was tried by the Senate. Since he had asked Ulysses to take over Stanton's cabinet post until the dispute was settled, Julia followed the proceedings with a more avid interest than she might normally have shown.

The President was acquitted by only one vote but Washington gossips were already saying that he would never be elected to another term in the White House. The Republicans, looking for a strong candidate for the election of 1868, turned to Ulysses Grant.

Ulysses did not attend the party's convention in Chicago but he was nominated by acclamation on the first ballot. He sent his acceptance by letter and although he was best known as a man of war, he now had only one goal for his battered country. "Let us have peace," he said.

A fever of activity surrounded the Presidential campaign but Ulysses took no part in it. Instead he and Julia went back to Galena to spend a quiet summer with their children. On the way they stopped off in St. Louis to tend to some business.

Colonel Dent had suffered a severe financial setback and was close to bankruptcy. He had managed to hold on to White Haven but most of its acreage had been sold off to pay his debts. At Julia's urging, Ulysses bought back the land and hired an overseer to run the farm on a businesslike basis.

Ulysses had resolved to stay in Galena until the election was over in the fall. As the day grew closer, Julia noticed that he was quieter and more thoughtful than ever. "Are you worried about the election?" she asked him one evening.

He took his pipe out of his mouth and said flatly, "I don't know which worries me more, winning or losing."

"You'll make a good President," Julia said confidently.

Ulysses reached over and touched her hand. "I'm glad you have so much faith in me," he said. "I wish I had more in myself."

On election night, Ulysses went down to Congressman Elihu Washburne's house to follow the returns as they came in over the telegraph. Julia stayed home with their two younger children and tried to keep her mind off the election. It was not easy. Jesse kept asking if there would be a place to keep his Shetland pony at the White House and Nellie wanted to know if she could have a new dress to wear to the inauguration.

"There'll be plenty of time to talk about that if your father wins," Julia told them. "Right now, I think you'd better scoot upstairs to bed."

Julia followed them up to be sure that the lamp was turned down and that Jesse was tucked under the covers. Then she returned to the parlor and settled down in front of the fire with some mending. It was almost two in the morning when she heard a key turn in the lock. She looked up to see Ulysses standing in the front hall. "It looks like I'm elected," he said quietly.

Ulysses went over, took her hand, and sat beside her on the sofa. Before he could tell her about the tremendous majority he had rolled up, a floorboard creaked on the staircase and ten-year-old Jesse leaned over the banister. "Did you win?" he hissed.

"Yes," Ulysses replied.

There was a loud cheer from the front hall and Jesse and Nellie tumbled down the stairs and rushed into their father's arms.

"I thought I sent you to bed hours ago!" Julia exclaimed, trying to sound cross.

Jesse flashed her an impudent grin and Nellie informed her airily that she couldn't possibly go to sleep without kissing the President of the United States goodnight.

XVII

JULIA MADE an inspection tour of the White House shortly before Ulysses' inauguration and came back shaking her head. The curtains were in tatters, the bathrooms needed to be modernized and there was not a single closet in the entire place. "We'll be a lot more comfortable," she said, "if we stay right here on I Street."

She refused to move until Congress appropriated enough money to bring the White House up to her standards.

The legislators were dubious at first about Julia's request for closets. The idea of built-in storage space was a new one; most people still kept their clothes in big wooden wardrobes. But eventually the Congressmen approved the appropriation and the remodeling got under way.

While the plumbers and carpenters were busy at the White House, the Grants remained in their home on I Street. When summer came they took a house in Long Branch, New Jersey, where they could enjoy the ocean breezes.

It was a happy summer. Fred came home from West Point for a few weeks, Buck was enjoying a vacation from Harvard, and Nellie had a good time letting Jesse drive her up and down Ocean Avenue in his pony cart.

The only sad note came in August when John Rawlins, who had become Ulysses' Secretary of War, died of tuberculosis. Julia and Ulysses still remembered how they had celebrated the surrender at Appomattox with John and his wife, Emma. They had double reason to grieve at his funeral: Emma also had the disease and would soon follow her husband to the grave.

By fall the White House was completely refurbished and the Grants moved in. When the butler appeared to announce dinner on their first evening in their new home, Ulysses offered Julia his arm. "It's quite a change from Hardscrabble, isn't it?" he whispered as he escorted her into the dining room.

Julia liked to entertain and with a chef and a staff of trained servants, she enjoyed it more than ever. She gave a twenty-nine-course dinner for Queen Victoria's son, Prince Arthur, and an equally splendid banquet for Grand Duke Alexis of Russia.

Her sole complaint about state dinners was the trouble she had persuading Ulysses to wear evening clothes. "I don't feel comfortable in them," he grumbled. When Julia pointed out how conspicuous he would look in a business suit when everyone else had on white tie and tails, he finally gave in.

It was customary for the First Lady to hold a reception one afternoon each week. Julia's were on Tuesdays and she insisted on throwing the White House doors open to everyone. An ordinary seamstress who came by trolley car was received as graciously as an ambassador's wife with a footman to help her out of her barouche.

Ulysses had been in office only six months when he was faced with his first crisis. His sister Virginia's husband, Abel Corbin, was involved with a pair of Wall Street speculators, James Fisk and Jay Gould, in a scheme to corner the gold market. Their plan was to buy gold at a low rate, send the market for it skyrocketing, and then sell out at a fat profit. The scheme could only be foiled if the United States Treasury released some of the Government's gold reserves. If there was more of the precious metal in circulation, the price would quickly plummet.

Abel Corbin sent his brother-in-law a frantic letter begging him to withhold the Treasury's gold. Ulysses decided it was wiser not to reply, but Julia wrote a cool note to Virginia. "My husband is annoyed by your husband's speculations," she said. "You must close them as quickly as you can."

Corbin, Fisk, and Gould sold out before the Treasury gold was released, but other investors were not so fortunate. The gold market collapsed and thousands of them went bankrupt. The day became known on Wall Street as Black Friday.

A rumor soon started that Ulysses Grant had also been involved in the scheme. Corbin was his brother-in-law and he was known to be friendly with Fisk and Gould. Julia, too, was suspect because her letter warning Abel Corbin to get out of the gold market had enabled all three of the speculators to escape without suffering any losses.

Julia was infuriated at the charges that were leveled at them, but Ulysses advised her to ignore them. "We've done nothing to be ashamed of," he said. Some months later, a Congressional investigation exonerated both the Grants of any wrongdoing.

In theory at least, the President was supposed to be able to relax in his living quarters on the second floor of the White House. But Ulysses maintained that things were more hectic up there than they were in his office.

Jesse had a lively group of friends who liked to romp through the house. On top of that, Colonel Dent now made his home with his daughter and her family.

Old age had made the Colonel more cantankerous than ever. The minute he arrived in the White House, he cast a critical eye on the china and sniffed, "You'll never get me to drink tea out of those cups. They're too coarse." Julia removed the offending cups and ordered them replaced with a more delicate set.

When it came to politics, Colonel Dent was less easy to please. He loved to find fault with Ulysses' cabinet members or with the way he was handling Congress. Ulysses, no longer offended by his father-in-law's tirades, simply buried himself in the *Washington Post* until Colonel Dent got tired and shuffled off to bed.

When Jesse Grant came to visit, Ulysses swore that he was afraid to come upstairs at all. Jesse and the Colonel both loved to argue and since they disagreed on almost everything, their conversation never failed to end in a fight.

Somehow Julia managed to remain serene in spite of the uproar. She supervised the busy household with efficiency and good humor and the servants agreed that she was the most gracious First Lady they had ever worked for.

When she was not tending her own family or presiding over some official function, Julia's principal pastime was visiting Washington's homes and hospitals. During the Christmas season she would descend on her favorite toy store with two or three dozen youngsters from a local orphanage in tow. "Pick out whatever you want," she would tell them.

The children would emerge with armloads of toys and a beaming Julia would order the bill sent to her at the White House. "And while you're at it," she would add, "send over some toy soldiers for Jesse."

Nellie Grant celebrated her fourteenth birthday the summer after her father was elected President. She was a slender girl with long brown hair and wide gentle eyes framed by thick dark lashes. Her father said she was the prettiest girl in Washington and when she appeared at her mother's receptions, the other guests usually agreed.

When Nellie was sixteen, Julia and Ulysses decided to send her to Miss Porter's School in Farmington, Connecticut. Ulysses insisted on taking her up on the train. "If we let your mother do it," he said, "she'll cry at the thought of leaving you and turn right around and bring you back."

Nellie promised to study hard and not to get homesick, but after the first few days she announced that she detested the place. "I shall die if I have to stay," she telegraphed her parents.

There were frantic messages from Washington imploring the new student to give Miss Porter's a longer trial, but Nellie was adamant. By Thanksgiving she was back in Washington, taking part in all the cotillions and driving in Rock Creek Park whenever it pleased her.

The gossips whispered that she was too young for such things and that her parents were spoiling her. Julia knew what they were saying but she refused to let it upset her. "I guess we do indulge Nellie too much," she admitted to Ulysses, "but I like to see the children having a good time."

Julia had never worried about her crossed eye until Ulysses became famous. Then she began wondering if something could be done about it. Not long after she moved into the White House she went to a surgeon in Washington.

"Yes," he told her, "there's a new operation. It's fairly

simple and I have every reason to believe it will correct your problem."

Julia made all the arrangements and went home with the news that she was to be admitted to the hospital the following week. Ulysses voiced no objections to the operation, but as the date grew closer he began to question her more closely about it. Was she sure the surgeon was a good man? Were there any risks involved? How did she know it would work?

Julia had more than a few misgivings herself, but she was determined to go through with the surgery. On the day she was to leave for the hospital, she resolutely packed her valise, put on her bonnet, and started for the door. She was just reaching for the knob when Ulysses, who had come upstairs to say good-bye, stepped in front of her.

"Julia," he said firmly, "I don't want you to have your eyes fooled with. They're all right just the way they are."

Julia was stunned. "But, Ulysses," she said, "I'm only having this done so I'll look prettier for you."

He shook his head. "Maybe this operation will make you look better to other people," he said, "but to me you're prettier as you are—the way you were when I first saw you."

He reached over and untied her bonnet strings. "I'll send a message to the surgeon not to expect you," he said.

Ulysses seemed surprised when Julia nodded obediently and took off her cloak. "You're not angry at me?" he asked her.

"Angry!" Julia exclaimed with a smile. "I was worried about the operation, too. I'm relieved that you won't let me have it."

XVIII

THE GRANTS enjoyed their first vacation at Long Branch so much that they decided to buy a house there. The Jersey shore resort was rapidly becoming as fashionable as Saratoga and Newport and the First Family's arrival assured its continued popularity.

The summer White House was usually referred to as a cottage. Actually it was an immense shingled house with a gabled roof and a wide octagonal porch that faced the Atlantic Ocean. Julia and Ulysses often sat out there and watched the steamboats that came in close to the shore to blow their whistles in salute to the President.

Julia was now in her forties and she was no longer the slim young lady Ulysses had courted at White Haven. In fact, he sometimes teased her about getting plump. One afternoon as they were sitting on the porch at Long Branch, he saw Buck leap lightly over the railing and go loping across the lawn to visit one of his friends. Ulysses turned to Julia with a mischievous smile.

"Did you see that?" he said. "Now suppose you were sitting here all alone and the cottage caught fire. If the front steps burned down, you'd never get out alive."

"That's what you think," Julia replied haughtily. Jumping up from her rocking chair, she scaled the porch railing as agilely as Buck had done and stood laughing up at her husband from the lawn below. "There," she said, "I'm not such a fat old woman after all."

Ulysses' first term in office was neither a huge success nor a dismal failure. He was criticized for appointing so many of his friends to public office and for failing to bring justice and order to the battered South. However, even his opponents had to admire the way he was paying the tremendous debt created by the Civil War and the way he had persuaded Great Britain to reimburse the American Government for damages inflicted on the Union Navy by English ships that were sold to the Confederates.

The Republicans nominated Ulysses Grant to run for a second term in 1872. He defeated his opponent, the New York newspaper editor Horace Greeley, by an overwhelming majority. Ulysses claimed there was only one drawback to his victory. "Now we have to face another inaugural ball," he groaned.

The Grants' first inaugural ball had been held in a recently completed wing of the Treasury Building. Some of the scaffolding was still up and the air was thick with dust left by the builders. Many of the guests seemed on the verge of choking to death and a couple of them actually fainted. To make matters worse, the ball was run so haphazardly that some of the guests never had any supper and many could not find their coats and hats when it was time to leave.

The second inaugural ball was equally disastrous. This time it was held in an exhibition hall called the Muslin Palace. The building was freezing cold. Julia, shivering in a new white brocade gown, wished she could have kept her wrap on as so many of the other guests did. No one wanted to drink the iced champagne that was served; they all ordered hot chocolate and coffee instead.

Julia was not responsible for planning either ball but she was embarrassed about them just the same. Ulysses, who disliked balls of any kind, did not care. "Now I know why Presidents never run for a third term," he remarked on the way home to the White House. "Going through two of these is quite enough."

The ensuing year was not a happy one for the Grants. Ulysses' father died in June and Colonel Dent passed away the following December. The family was still in mourning when more bad news reached the White House. Ulysses' former Vice President, Schuyler Colfax, and several of his close friends in Congress were implicated in a fraud. They had taken money intended to finance the Union Pacific Railroad and put it into a bogus company of their own, called Crédit Mobilier.

The Crédit Mobilier scandal was followed in the headlines by still another misfortune. The firm of Jay Cooke and Company, one of the country's leading banks, was forced to close its doors. A number of other companies followed suit, unemployment resulted, and the country was in the grip of the Panic of 1873.

Ulysses blamed himself for the unhappy events that were dogging his career as President. "Sometimes I think that circumstances have forced me into a job that's more than I can handle," he said.

Julia, with her usual loyalty, stood up for him. "It's not your fault," she said. "It's just bad luck."

In the spring of 1874, public attention was again focussed on the White House, but this time not because of a scandal. Nellie Grant was engaged to be married. She had taken a tour of Europe with some friends of her parents and on the way home had met and fallen in love with a handsome young Englishman named Algernon Sartoris.

Ulysses and Julia both had doubts about the match. For one thing, Nellie was only nineteen. For another, Algy did not seem like the solid, stable kind of husband they had always hoped Nellie would choose.

When Algy asked Ulysses Grant for permission to marry his daughter, the President insisted that he needed some time to discuss the matter with his wife. "I don't know what to say," he told Julia. "I don't like the young man, but what does that mean? Your father was opposed to our wedding and look how wrong he was."

Julia agreed that the prospects for a happy marriage seemed dim. "But perhaps Nellie knows her own heart better than we do," she sighed. "Let's not stand in their way."

The wedding date was set for May twenty-first. Both Nellie and Julia were in a dither for weeks before the ceremony. A wedding dress had to be selected and fitted, bridesmaids outfitted, and a trousseau collected. Gifts began pouring in from all over the world and Nellie, in the midst of the parties that were constantly being given in her honor, had to be reminded to sit down and write thank-you notes. "Being a bride is hard work," her mother told her. "But there'll be time enough to rest when you and Algy are off in Europe on your honeymoon."

The wedding was held in the East Room of the White House. It was decorated with masses of flowers and ferns; a special platform was erected at one end for the bride and groom to stand on while they took their vows. A wedding bell of white roses hung from the ceiling above it and the floor was carpeted with an oriental rug that had been given to the Grants by the Sultan of Turkey.

Julia was upset because Algy Sartoris insisted on carrying a small bouquet of his own for the occasion. She tried to ignore it and instead kept her eyes fixed on Nellie, who looked radiant in a white satin gown and a veil of Brussels lace.

Julia thought she spied a tear on Ulysses' cheek as he escorted his daughter to her waiting bridegroom. Later when the wedding breakfast was over and the newlyweds had left on their honeymoon, she found him sitting by himself in Nellie's room, staring gloomily at the floor. Julia walked over and laid her hand on his shoulder. "I'll miss her, too," she said softly.

Ulysses reached up and stroked her fingers. "It's not that so much," he murmured. "I just wish she'd fallen in love with someone else."

There was a second wedding in the family the following autumn. Fred, who had graduated from West Point and was now a lieutenant colonel in the army, married a girl from Chicago named Ida Honoré. This time Julia and Ulysses had no doubts about the match. "She's a lovely girl," Julia told her son. "I know you'll be very happy."

With Fred and Nellie both gone, the White House seemed strangely quiet. Buck had graduated from Harvard and was living in New York and attending Columbia Law School. Jesse had just entered Cornell University.

Julia complained about being lonesome, but she enjoyed the chance to spend more time with Ulysses. Occasionally they sat in the parlor holding hands as they had done in the early years of their marriage; in the morning, they strolled in to breakfast arm in arm. Afterward, Ulysses usually lingered in Julia's sitting room to talk for a few more minutes before going downstairs to his desk.

The house was not empty for long. Nellie returned from her honeymoon and she and Algy decided to remain in Washington for a while. Then Fred was assigned to the White House staff and he and Ida came home to live. The two young matrons soon joined Julia on the receiving line at her afternoon receptions.

Ulysses was doing his best to be a good Chief Executive, but his administration continued to be plagued by scandals. The most spectacular one occurred in 1875 when it was discovered that internal revenue agents in St. Louis had been involved in a conspiracy with a group of whiskey distillers to defraud the Government of taxes.

A report on the operations of the Whiskey Ring, as the conspiracy was called, was sent to the White House, but nothing was done about it. Eventually, it was disclosed that Ulysses' personal secretary, General Orville Babcock, had been bribed to see that the report never reached the President's desk.

The disclosure was a personal as well as a political blow. Orville Babcock had been on Ulysses' staff since Civil War days and the Grants regarded him as one of their dearest friends. They were equally disturbed because the news of the Whiskey Ring's operations all but destroyed Ulysses' reputation in Missouri. He had planned to retire to White Haven when his career in the White House was over. Now he did not have the heart to face his old friends in St. Louis.

The Whiskey Ring was by no means the last of the scandals. Secretary of War William Belknap, in charge of selling Indian trading posts in the West, was found guilty of accepting kickbacks from the buyers. Ulysses Grant's critics again shook their heads and accused him of being too easily deceived by his friends.

The year 1876 marked Ulysses' last full year in the White House. Julia would always remember it for another reason. Fred's wife, Ida, gave birth to a little girl. She was Ulysses' and Julia's first grandchild and she was christened Julia Dent Grant.

Little Julia was born in the White House and baptized in the East Room. On her grandmother's last New Year's Day reception in 1877, she was carried downstairs to be shown off to the guests in a white lace dress that Julia herself had worn as an infant at White Haven.

The new year brought a new occupant to the White House. Ulysses and Julia gave a formal dinner to welcome President-elect Rutherford B. Hayes. Julia escorted Mrs. Hayes on a tour of the mansion, and pointed with special pride to the closets. "I had to fight with Congress to get them," she said, "but it was well worth the battle."

Now that his term of office was over, Ulysses wanted to take Julia on a trip around the world. "Can we afford it?" was the first thing she asked.

"I think we can manage," Ulysses assured her. He had invested some money in the stock market. The income from that plus the rent they still received from White Haven would be enough to support them for the present.

The prospect of the journey made it easier for Julia to leave the White House. She had fond memories of the eight years they had spent there. "I'll miss it," she sighed as they drove out the front gate for the last time and headed down Pennsylvania Avenue.

Ulysses' own memories were overshadowed by the realization that he had not been as strong a President as he had hoped to be. "I won't miss it at all," he said, settling back in the carriage. "I'm glad to leave it behind."

XIX

THE FORMER PRESIDENT and his wife sailed for Europe in May, 1877. Their first stop was England, where Queen Victoria honored them with an impressive dinner at Windsor Castle. Nellie was living not far away at Southampton and despite her parents' forebodings, appeared to be still in love with Algy and quite content with English country life.

The Grants toured England and Scotland for several weeks and then crossed the channel to see the rest of Europe. Julia was captivated by the scenery in Switzerland and vowed she would never forget her first sight of the snowcapped Alps towering over the church spires of Geneva. But she enjoyed herself most in Paris.

"What shall we do first?" Ulysses asked her as soon as they were settled in their suite at the Bristol Hotel.

"Go shopping, of course," Julia told him with a twinkle in her eye.

Before they left the French capital, Julia had added several new outfits to her wardrobe. Between fittings, she also managed to visit all the historic churches and museums that were listed in their guide book.

They spent the winter in Egypt. When they arrived in Cairo they were greeted by the viceroy, who invited them to stay in one of his palaces and provided an army of servants to wait on them. They encountered the same hospitality everywhere they went. They were received by kings and queens, presented with lavish gifts and feted with parades and banquets.

Ulysses had never enjoyed being the center of attention, but Julia started to notice a change in his attitude. Instead of looking stiff and uncomfortable, he began to smile and wave to the crowds. "I think you're finally getting used to being a public figure," she told him.

Back home, the news of Ulysses and Julia's reception in Europe was making Americans take a new look at their Civil War hero. The scandals that had clouded his years in the White House were soon forgotten and he was again spoken of with respect and affection. Some of the leaders of the Republican party even began talking about nominating him for the Presidency again.

For the moment, though, Ulysses was enjoying himself too much to think about politics. After touring Europe, he was anxious to sail through the Suez Canal and continue eastward to the Orient. "The Orient!" Julia exclaimed. "At this rate we'll never get home!"

They had been gone almost two years. Although she missed her family occasionally, Julia too was having the time of her life. Part of her pleasure came from seeing Ulysses so happy. He looked healthier and more relaxed than she had seen him in years.

Their first stop on the voyage eastward was India, where Julia fell ill with a mild case of tropical fever. While she was recovering she kept herself and Ulysses amused by drawing up a make-believe will in which she left four million dollars to Ulysses to buy ice-cream knives and umbrella handles for her friends back home.

At Tientsin, China, Julia was flattered to discover that

the viceroy's wife had invited the women from the American colony to a dinner in her honor.

"None of them have ever been to the royal palace before," Julia told Ulysses. "They're all wondering how to dress."

Ulysses, who had no interest in such matters, shook his head. "My only advice is not to wear anything too fancy," he said, "or the viceroy's wife will start complaining that her husband isn't outfitting her in proper style."

In the end Julia decided to wear her best clothes and jewelry; she advised the other American women to do the same. The viceroy's wife complimented them, through her interpreter, on their elegant clothes and beautiful pins and earrings. The women were even more enchanted with their hostess's outfit—a pair of brocade trousers and a tunic encrusted with jewels.

Japan was the final and most spectacular stop on the Grants' itinerary. The Japanese minister in Washington was called home to direct the arrangements for their visit. The streets were adorned with colorful lanterns and the visitors were greeted with fireworks and pageants everywhere they went.

On the fourth of July, the Emperor invited his guests to a state dinner at the Imperial Palace. Julia was fascinated by the lovely furnishings. She sat on a delicate black lacquered sofa inlaid with golden chrysanthemums. Rubbing her fingers gently over its silken finish, she told the Emperor how much she admired it. He bowed graciously and insisted that she accept the sofa, and the chairs that matched it, as a gift from the people of Japan. To Julia's astonishment, the furniture was crated and shipped to America on the same boat that brought them home.

The returning travelers steamed into San Francisco Bay

on a bright September day in 1879. Ulysses had sailed home from the same port when he had resigned from the army twenty-five years before. He had been discouraged and penniless then and above all, unbearably lonely. Now a brass band greeted him at the pier and throngs of jubilant admirers almost drowned out its music with their cheers.

"This is a warmer welcome than we've received anywhere in the world," Julia said happily. "It's nice to be home."

The Grants planned to return to Galena but they wanted to do some touring in their own country first. They visited the redwood forests in California, drove through Yosemite Park, and made a stop in Virginia City, Nevada, where the famous Comstock Lode had been discovered in 1859.

Silver mining was still the town's major industry, and a visit to one of the mines had been arranged as part of the Grants' official welcome. Julia eyed the rickety platform that would carry them down into the unlit mine-shaft and seriously considered returning to her hotel room. Then the young man who was serving as their escort came up to her. "You're going down into the mine, aren't you, Mrs. Grant?" he said. "Your husband thinks you're afraid but I don't believe it."

"Of course I'm not afraid," Julia replied, concealing her nervousness with an eager smile. "I've always wanted to visit a silver mine."

The former First Lady donned an old shirt to keep her dress from getting dusty, took a lantern and joined their guide on the expedition through the subterranean passageways. Later, she discovered that Ulysses had bet a dollar that she would not do it. "That was a wicked thing to do," she told him good-naturedly. "You deserved to lose."

Ulysses and Julia were back in Galena when the Republican Convention met in the summer of 1880. Ulysses' name was put in nomination for the Presidency, but on the final ballot the majority of the votes went to James A. Garfield. Although Julia found it hard to conceal her disappointment, Ulysses had no regrets. "I'll escape four years of hard work and four years of abuse," he said. "I'm happy to give my support to Garfield."

A group of the former President's admirers had raised enough money to buy him a house in New York, where he had become a partner in a Wall Street brokerage house. The company, Grant & Ward, had been organized by Buck and two friends of his, James Fish and Ferdinand Ward. No longer on active duty with the army, Fred had also invested in the firm.

Julia soon decided that she liked living in a town house in New York almost as much as living in the White House. Situated on East Sixty-sixth Street just a few steps away from Fifth Avenue, the house was crammed with mementoes and souvenirs the Grants had collected through the years.

The sitting room boasted the black lacquer furniture that had been given to Julia by the Emperor of Japan and a gold lacquer cabinet—another gift from the Emperor—that was over eleven hundred years old. The leather-bound books in the library were a present to Ulysses from the people of Boston and the floor of Julia's room was covered with a Bengal tiger skin that had been presented to the Grants in India.

Ulysses and Julia had many old friends in New York and they went to almost as many parties and receptions as they had in Washington. In addition, Julia had her grandchildren to keep her busy. Along with his daughter, Julia, Fred now had a son named Ulysses. Buck and Jesse were each married and Jesse had a little girl named Nellie.

Nellie Grant Sartoris had three children, two girls and a boy. They came back to visit in the United States at least once a year. When they did, Julia treated them as she did the other children, plying them with candy and toys and giving them everything they asked for.

"You're spoiling them," Nellie always admonished her.

"Of course I am," Julia would reply stoutly. "That's what grandmothers are for."

Ulysses' mother, Hannah Grant, had steadfastly refused to visit her son in the White House, but she was always happy to welcome him and his family to her own home in Covington. After her husband died, she left Kentucky and settled in New Jersey with her daughter Virginia. She died in Jersey City in 1883.

A year later, her oldest son received a staggering blow to his fortunes. The firm of Grant & Ward had been prospering and for the first time in his life, Ulysses was a rich man. Then one Sunday morning, his partner Ferdinand Ward appeared at the house on Sixty-sixth Street with some bad news. The bank that handled the firm's accounts was on the brink of failure. If he and Ulysses could not raise $300,000 at once, the bank would close and their own firm would be wiped out in the bargain.

Ward promised to raise half the money; Ulysses agreed to raise the other half. He had no trouble doing it. His friend William Vanderbilt lived just a few blocks away. Ulysses walked over to his mansion on Fifth Avenue and asked if he could borrow $150,000. The millionaire, who was a great admirer of the former general, sat down and wrote out a check without a moment's hesitation. Ulysses gave it to Ferdinand Ward and assumed that the crisis was over.

When he arrived at his office on Monday morning, however, an ever graver disaster awaited him. Ward had absconded with Ulysses' $150,000. He and James Fish had also cleaned out all the money and securities in the firm's safe and had even taken a jar of twenty-dollar gold pieces that Julia had placed on the mantel of her husband's office for good luck.

Fred and Buck sat at their desks, dazed and shaken. "We're completely ruined," Buck said in a hollow voice. "We don't even have enough to pay the rent."

The news of the Grants' financial disaster made instant headlines. One of Ulysses' old friends called on him to offer his sympathies. After he left, Ulysses found a check for a thousand dollars lying on a table in the parlor. A few days later, a man whom he had never met sent him another check for a thousand dollars. He called it a "loan on account of my share for services ending April, 1865."

Despite his own financial losses, Ulysses was determined to repay the $150,000 he had borrowed from William Vanderbilt. Julia agreed that they should offer him the deeds to White Haven and to the house in Galena, along with Ulysses' mementoes of the Civil War.

At first Vanderbilt refused to accept their offer but when he saw how determined Ulysses was to discharge his debt, he agreed. He kept the deeds but insisted that the war relics be given to the Smithsonian Institute in Washington.

The collection included the shoulder straps that Julia had snipped from Ulysses' overcoat after the siege of Richmond, a gold medal he had received for capturing Vicksburg, and a model of the table on which Robert E. Lee had signed the articles of surrender at Appomattox.

There were tears in Julia's eyes as she watched the mementoes being carried out of the house, but Ulysses remained impassive. "They're not really ours," he reminded her. "They belong to the country."

At the first sign of summer, the Grants closed up their house in New York and moved to Long Branch where they could live more cheaply. Fred and his family, who had been forced to give up their own house, moved in with them. The servants were let go and Julia, with Ida to assist her, took over the housework and cooking herself. "I've done it before," she said brightly. "I can do it again."

Ulysses spent the first part of the summer sitting on the front porch gazing out at the ocean and trying to devise a way to earn some money. The situation appeared to be hopeless until one afternoon an editor of *The Century* magazine, Robert Johnson, came to see him. Would General Grant write a series of articles for *The Century* about the Civil War?

Ulysses knew nothing about writing, but he knew more than any man in the world about the Civil War. "I'm not sure that I can do it," he told Johnson, "but I'm too desperately in need of money not to try."

XX

JULIA MOVED an old kitchen table into one room of the sprawling beach cottage and Ulysses got out his old war maps and diaries and set to work. At first his writing style was plodding and difficult to follow, but Robert Johnson came to visit him again and made some suggestions for improving it. "Pretend you're talking about it," he said, "not writing it down."

Ulysses took Johnson's advice and soon developed a clear, lively style. The editor said he was as good as some of the professional writers he worked with.

Ulysses' first article was on the battle of Shiloh. Its publication increased *The Century*'s circulation by fifty thousand copies and the editor-in-chief, Richard Watson Gilder, happily doubled Ulysses' fee for the series. The rest of the articles were equally well received and Gilder asked him to expand the articles and publish them as a book.

Ulysses showed his letter to Julia. "After all the different kinds of work I've done in my lifetime," he said with a smile, "it looks as though I'm finally going to wind up as an author."

It was a job he enjoyed. Sometimes he became so engrossed in his writing that he insisted on working at night and on Sundays. Julia never complained. She had her two grandchildren to keep her company. Young Julia liked to be read to and Ulysses, an erstwhile gardener, always needed help with his melon vines or tomato plants.

Richard Watson Gilder offered Ulysses a contract for his memoirs, but before Ulysses had a chance to sign it, his old friend Mark Twain heard about the book and came to him with a more lucrative offer from his own publishers. "I don't like to desert *The Century,*" Ulysses said, "but in my present financial condition I don't think I have much choice."

The weather at Long Branch was especially fine that summer. When Ulysses was not working on his book, he and Julia sat on the front porch and reminisced about the past. They talked about White Haven and Galena, the grim years of the Civil War and glamorous ones in the White House.

Ulysses teased Julia about the quilt she had started making and never finished, and Julia teased him right back about the day he had come calling at White Haven with his uniform dripping wet.

One afternoon they were sitting lazily on the porch and Ulysses was eating a peach. Suddenly he let out a sharp cry of pain. "What is it?" Julia asked in alarm.

He shook his head and seemed baffled. There had been a strange stabbing sensation in his mouth. The pain recurred several times during the summer, but Ulysses put off going to a doctor until they moved back to New York in the fall. The specialist he consulted then examined him carefully and diagnosed his condition as "serious epithelial trouble."

"What does that mean," Ulysses asked bluntly, "cancer?"

The doctor was equally frank. "Yes," he replied gravely.

Determined not to worry Julia, Ulysses told her the throat condition was only a minor complaint. However, when it did not clear up after several weeks of treatment, she began to suspect that it might be something more serious. She continued to hope for his recovery, but as the pain in his throat grew worse, she began to face the fact that her husband was dying.

Ulysses, who had been aware of his condition for months, went calmly on with the business of writing his memoirs. While he worked, Julia moved around quietly, making sure that he had everything he wanted, and ushering his many visitors in and out of the house. Cump Sherman was a regular caller. So was Simon Buckner, the Confederate general who had surrendered to him at Fort Donelson. "I ought to tell my side of that battle for your book," Buckner said. "It was tough being up against a fighter like you."

Ulysses was still a fighter. He was in constant pain, but he sat at his desk each day writing until his fingers grew numb and his eyes burned from the effort. Everyone in the family contributed to the project. Fred, who still lived with his parents, helped with the research. Ida read aloud from the various reference books he needed and Julia took young Julia and Ulysses walking in Central Park so they would not disturb their grandfather while he worked.

Ulysses grew steadily worse. He found it a struggle to eat and lost over twenty pounds. Still he kept doggedly on with his book. "If you ever take the time to read it," he wrote to Nellie in England, "you'll find out what sort of a boy and man I was before you remember me."

Before long, the newspapers got wind of Ulysses Grant's illness and soon the whole country knew that he was doomed. Out of sympathy, Congress restored his old rank of general which he had given up when he became President.

Julia came into his room waving the telegram above her head. "Hooray," she cried, "they've brought back our old commander!"

Ulysses was pleased with the honor but he was even more grateful for the salary that went with it. "That ought to keep the wolf away from the door," he told Julia in the hoarse croak he had developed since his illness.

A few weeks later, Ulysses discovered that he could look forward to even greater prosperity. Even though his book was still unfinished, his publishers had already started taking orders for it. Ulysses and Julia were flabbergasted to learn that the advance sales totalled over three hundred thousand dollars.

By June, 1885, the memoirs were close to being finished. Julia decided not to make their usual trip to Long Branch. Instead, she bundled Ulysses onto a private railroad car and the whole family left to spend the summer in upper New York State. One of the Grants' friends, Joseph Drexel, had offered them his cottage at Mount McGregor, just above Lake George. Ulysses liked the clear mountain air and the breathtaking view, but most of the time he was too sick to enjoy it. Talking became so painful that he took to writing down whatever he had to say. "All my physicians or any number of them can do for me now," he scrawled on the scratchpad he kept at his side, "is to make my burden of pain as light as possible."

In the middle of July, Ulysses' memoirs were finally completed. Julia knew that his determination to finish the two volumes was all that had kept him alive. Now he was ready to die.

The end came on the morning of July twenty-third. Julia, who was at his bedside, was consoled by the fact that after his long agony, his death was swift and painless. Afterward, she found a letter in the pocket of his robe, and a tiny gold case containing a lock of her hair. "I bid you a final farewell," the letter said, "until we meet in another and, I trust, better world."

Later Julia discovered that Ulysses had written instructions to Fred about the arrangements for his funeral. "Wherever my tomb might be," he said, "a place shall be reserved for your mother at my side."

Julia remained composed during the simple funeral service that was held at Mount McGregor, but she was too grief-stricken to attend the more elaborate ceremonies that preceded her husband's burial in New York. There was a slow solemn procession up Broadway; buildings were draped in black and people turned out by the thousands to pay their respects. William Tecumseh Sherman and Simon Buckner were among the pallbearers, and the mourners included the President, Grover Cleveland, and two former Presidents, Rutherford B. Hayes and Chester A. Arthur.

A group of prominent New Yorkers arranged for Ulysses to be buried in Riverside Park and raised the money to build an imposing tomb on the site. Julia helped select the inscription that was carved on its stone facade. It was a line from Ulysses' letter of acceptance when he was first nominated for the Presidency: Let Us Have Peace.

Julia was fifty-nine when her husband died. Her brown hair had turned to gray and her eyes had grown weaker, but she remained as gracious and warmhearted as ever.

A few years after Ulysses' death she learned that Mrs. Jefferson Davis had taken up residence in New York.

Julia went to call on her and the two widows soon became good friends. Sometimes they went driving together and occasionally they stopped for a visit at Ulysses' tomb on Riverside Drive. "I'll be joining him there someday," Julia told Varina Davis with a matter-of-fact smile.

Ulysses' *Memoirs,* published shortly after his death, earned almost half a million dollars and made Julia a wealthy woman. Eventually she sold her house in New York and moved to Washington, where she continued to take great delight in her children and grandchildren.

In 1893, Jesse and his wife moved to California. He raved so much about the climate that Buck and his family followed him out. Fred traveled even farther afield. He served as the United States Minister in Vienna for several years and later went to the Philippines with the army to put down the insurrection that occurred in the islands after the Spanish-American War. Fred was promoted to major general for his service in the Philippines. When Julia heard the news she remembered that her father had always said he'd grow up to be a general some day.

Julia's favorite cousin Caroline O'Fallon died in 1898. Julia did not return to St. Louis for the funeral but sent a touching letter to Cousin Caroline's son John. "She was the beautiful angel of my childhood," she wrote. "So many acts of kindness, so many kind words of hers fill my heart's memory. Do you know your dear mother brought me my beautiful wedding gown and with such sweet, kind words—they still linger with me."

But although Julia had rich memories of the past, she also took a keen interest in everything that was going on in the present. She had a dozen grandchildren to fuss over and she never missed a chance to send pocket money to the boys and pretty clothes to the girls. She was on hand when her first grandchild, Julia, made her debut in Washington. When Julia married a dashing Russian nobleman a few years later, her grandmother, still lively at seventy-three, received almost as much attention as the bride.

To Julia's sorrow, the Grants' premonitions about their daughter's marriage to Algernon Sartoris finally came true. The couple separated shortly after Ulysses' death and Nellie returned to America with her family and became her mother's closest companion.

In the fall of 1902, Julia was stricken with a severe attack of bronchitis. The seventy-six-year-old widow was never really well again, but she bore her illness with her usual cheerful resignation. Julia died peacefully on December fourteenth with Nellie at her side. Her funeral services were held in Washington, but she was buried beside Ulysses in the tomb on Riverside Drive, close to her husband in death just as she had been in life.